Parking and Access at General Hospitals

ENO FOUNDATION FOR TRANSPORTATION, INC.

WESTPORT · 1973 · CONNECTICUT

Parking and Access at General Hospitals

GEORGE E. KANAAN

Staff Engineer

ENO FOUNDATION FOR TRANSPORTATION, INC.

WESTPORT · 1973 · CONNECTICUT

FOREWORD

Traffic problems have become deep concerns of hospital administrators and public authorities. To assist in this matter, the Eno Foundation is pleased to publish this report. It is an extension of *Access and Parking at Institutions* published by the Foundation in 1960. At that time relatively little research on hospital traffic had been undertaken. The data for the present report were found largely in individual traffic studies at hospitals.

Traffic characteristics vary widely between hospitals of different types. By limiting this study mostly to *general* hospitals, it was assumed that basic homogeneities in institutional structure and, therefore, in traffic characteristics exist. Whether the wide variations noted in some areas are caused by differences in general hospital operations, or by the inherent limitations of the data can only be determined by additional research. It is hoped, however, that the general hospital traffic planning criteria presented will have useful applications.

Many professionals have contributed to this study through advice, encouragement, and the provision of useful data. Their assistance is gratefully acknowledged.

Eno Foundation for Transportation, Inc.

TABLE OF CONTENTS

LIST OF TABLES

LIST OF FIGURES

x

xi

Chapter I

INTRODUCTION

Hospitals are major activity centers. In the United States they employ 2.9 million workers supported by nearly one million volunteers.[1] Daily they attract 15 million automobile trips generating about 55 million vehicle miles of travel.

Affluence, advances in medicine and surgery, the advent of medical insurance and governmental health programs, and the greater proportion of older people in the population all lead to a phenomenal increase in hospital use. Admissions to U.S. hospitals have grown by 67 percent in two and one-half decades from 91 admissions per 1,000 population per year in 1946 to 156 in 1970. In addition, the number of outpatient visits to U.S. hospitals increased from 246 visits per 1,000 population in 1962 to 447 in 1970. Figure 1 shows this annual growth of hospital visitations by inpatients and outpatients. Admissions, in this case, is the total number of patients accepted for inpatient (bed) service during a year (not including newborn). Outpatients are those who visit the hospital for clinical or emergency treatment but are not admitted as inpatients receiving overnight care.

The increasing number of hospital patients each year has been accompanied by increases in hospital services. The number of community hospitals (mostly general hospitals), for example, grew 8.4 percent in the last decade with an accompanying growth of 32.7 percent in the number of beds.

All this, in addition to the fact that many of the expanding older institutions are located in highly populated areas, has

1 *From Hospitals, J.A.H.A.:* Reprinted, with permission, from *Hospitals, Journal of the American Hospital Association* (Vol. 45, No. 15, Part 2, August 1971, pp. 447, 448, 460).

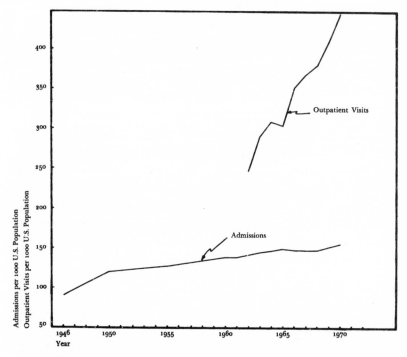

FIGURE 1.   U.S. hospital admissions 1946–1970 and outpatient visits 1962–1970
From Hospitals, J.A.H.A.: Reprinted, with permission, from *Hospitals, Journal
of the American Hospital Association* (Vol. 45, No. 15, Part 2, August 1971,
p. 460; and Vol. 44, No. 15, Part 1, August 1970, p. 472).

added to the traffic problems found at hospitals. The worsening
parking situation at hospitals has become to one hospital administrator more of a "problem than the nuisance it was."
The director of the University Hospitals of Cleveland was
quoted as saying, "the absence of adequate parking would
seriously affect our ability to recruit certain categories of
personnel."[2] Other major traffic concerns at hospitals include
patient access and expeditious handling of emergency vehicle
arrivals.

[2] Allen Fonoroff and Franklin Adler, *A Parking Program for University Circle*
(Cleveland, Ohio: University Circle Development Foundation, June 1965) p. 1.

Classes of Hospitals

Hospitals may be classified by: (1) type of control, (2) average length of stay by patients, and (3) the medical services provided. Table I shows the distribution of U.S. hospitals according to these three criteria. Half of these hospitals are controlled by nongovernmental, nonprofit bodies and 39 percent are operated by governmental agencies. The remaining 11 percent are run by private groups on a profit basis.

Hospitals offering general medical and surgical services constitute the majority (85 percent) of the institutions listed in Table I. Other specialized hospitals include maternity, children's, orthopedic, etc.

The short-stay hospitals (in which 50 percent of all patients stay less than 30 days) listed in Table I constitute 87 percent of the total number of hospitals and 99 percent of those classed as general hospitals.

Clearly, short-stay, nonfederal, general hospitals are the most numerous. The distribution of these hospitals by size, measured by the number of beds, is shown in Table II. Most have less than 200 beds and, of these, the greatest number belong to the 50-99 bed class. Regardless of the size of these short-stay hospitals, they will be referred to in this report as *general* hospitals, and it is with this type of institution that this report is mainly concerned.

The growth of community hospitals (mostly general hospitals) in the past decade is reflected in Table III. Their growth was accompanied by an overall decline in all other hospital categories. This trend is consistent with the prevailing philosophy within the health care industry that general hospital services should be expanded to provide not only general services but many specialized ones as well.

Inpatient Occupancy and Stay

Table IV shows the percent of occupancy in nongovernmental nonprofit general hospitals for each year from 1946 to

TABLE I—DISTRIBUTION OF U.S. HOSPITALS BY SERVICE, CONTROL, AND LENGTH OF STAY, 1970

Service	Federal		State Government		Local Government		Nonfederal Nongovernment for Profit		Nongovernment Nonprofit		Total Nonfederal		Total	
	Short Stay	Long Stay	Short Stay	Long Stay	Short Stay	Long Stay	Short Stay	Long Stay	Short Stay	Long Stay	Short Stay	Long Stay	Short Stay	Long Stay
General	333	38	141	8	1543	13	734	4	3243	12	5661	37	5994	75
Psychiatric	—	33	16	315	4	16	43	39	30	56	93	426	93	459
Tuberculosis	1	2	—	50	—	44	—	1	—	6	—	101	1	103
Other special	—	1	11	36	9	51	35	2	143	110	198	199	198	200
Total	334	74	168	409	1556	124	812	46	3416	184	5952	763	6286	837

From Hospitals, J.A.H.A.: Reprinted, with permission, from Hospitals, Journal of the American Hospital Association (Vol. 45, No. 15, Part 2, August 1971, p. 463).

TABLE II—DISTRIBUTION OF SHORT-STAY, GENERAL, NONFEDERAL
HOSPITALS BY SIZE, 1970

Type of Control

Number of Beds	Non-government Nonprofit	Local Government	State Government	Non-government Profit	Total
6–24	114	123	9	107	353
25–49	519	490	33	250	1292
50–99	714	481	29	223	1447
100–199	808	270	27	117	1222
200–299	470	72	6	30	578
300–399	296	39	9	—	344
400–499	156	22	10	—	188
Over 500	166	46	18	—	230
Total	3243	1543	141	727[a]	5654

a Excludes 7 hospitals having more than 300 beds and not classified by size.

From Hospitals, J.A.H.A.: Reprinted, with permission from *Hospitals, Journal of the American Hospital Association* (Vol. 45, No. 15, Part 2, August 1971, pp. 464–465).

TABLE III—GROWTH OF COMMUNITY HOSPITALS, 1960–1970[a]

Statistic	Year 1960	Year 1970	Percent Change
Hospitals	5407	5895	+ 8.4
Beds (thousands)	639	848	+32.7
Admissions (thousands)	22970	29252	+27.4
Out-patient visits (thousands)	70727	133545	+88.8
Personnel (thousands)	1080	1824[b]	+68.9
Average size (beds)	118	145	+22.9

a See definition in glossary at end of chapter.
b 1969 figure; 1970 was not available.

From Hospitals, J.A.H.A.: Reprinted, with permission from *Hospitals, Journal of the American Hospital Association* (Vol. 45, No. 15, Part 2, August 1971, p. 447).

TABLE IV—TRENDS IN OCCUPANCY, AVERAGE LENGTH OF STAY, AND
PERSONNEL AT GENERAL HOSPITALS, 1946–1970[a]

Year	Occupancy Percent	Average Length of Stay Days	Personnel (full-time equivalents) per 100 Patients (census)
1946	76.7	8.8	156
1950	74.4	7.7	191
1955	73.0	7.5	210
1960	76.6	7.4	232
1961	76.1	7.5	240
1962	76.8	7.5	241
1963	77.7	7.6	244
1964	78.1	7.6	247
1965	77.8	7.7	252
1966	78.5	7.9	264
1967	79.7	8.2	268
1968	80.0	8.3	276
1969	80.8	8.2	284
1970	80.1	8.2	292

[a] Data refer to nongovernmental, nonprofit, general hospitals only.

From Hospitals, J.A.H.A.: Reprinted, with permission from *Hospitals, Journal of the American Hospital Association* (Vol. 44, No. 15, Part 1, August 1970, p. 472; and Vol. 45, No. 15, Part 2, August 1971, p. 460).

1971. Occupancy is defined as the percentage ratio of the *census* to the number of hospital beds. A hospital *census* is the average daily number of patients (usually for the calendar year) receiving inpatient service, not including the newborn.

Both the occupancy rate and average length of stay remained fairly constant during the period covered by Table IV. However, both vary among individual hospitals. Table V shows that occupancy rates vary directly with the hospital size up to 200 beds after which they level off. The average occupancy rate for all hospital sizes is 80.3 percent.

TABLE V—VARIATIONS IN OCCUPANCY AND AVERAGE STAY BY SIZE OF
GENERAL HOSPITAL, 1970[a]

Number of Beds	Occupancy Percent	Average Stay Days
6–24	52.8	6.7
25–49	63.0	6.8
50–99	72.0	7.5
100–199	76.9	7.6
200–299	81.1	8.0
300–399	83.3	8.3
400–499	85.2	8.5
Over 500	84.8	9.6
All	80.3	8.2

[a] Data refer to nongovernmental, nonprofit, general hospitals only.

From Hospitals, J.A.H.A.: Reprinted, with permission from Hospitals, Journal of the American Hospital Association (Vol. 45, No. 15, Part 2, August 1971, pp. 464–465).

HOSPITAL PERSONNEL

It is customary to relate the size of the personnel force of a general hospital to the average daily number of inpatients and, also, to the number of hospital beds. These ratios are called personnel utilization rates. The personnel utilization rate for the average general hospital in 1970 would be (292/100) times (80.1/100) or 2.34 employees per hospital bed (see Table IV). However, this average ratio of employees to hospital beds cannot be used for traffic planning purposes because it varies greatly between individual hospitals.

Personnel totals for U.S. hospitals utilized in this report do not include students, interns, residents, or volunteers, but these account for only a small percentage of general hospital traffic activity. Those included in the totals are mostly supervisory nursing staff, nurses, aids, and orderlies. In most hospitals, these service groups work in three shifts (7 a.m. to 3:30 p.m.; 3 p.m. to 11:30 p.m.; and 11:15 p.m. to 7:15 a.m.). The first shift is the largest—employing about one-half of the total nursing staff—while the third shift is the smallest.

Office employees generally work from 8 a.m. to 4:30 p.m. or from 8:30 a.m. to 5 p.m.

OUTPATIENTS AND VISITORS

No method based on occupancy and bed statistics exists for estimating the number of outpatients who receive medical treatment in a general hospital. This number depends on the clinical activity of a given hospital.

On the average, about one-third of all outpatient visits are made to emergency rooms.[3] However, there is a growing trend toward the establishment of medical office buildings within hospital complexes where doctors engage in private practice and serve on the hospital medical staff as well.

Outpatient visitation depends on clinic schedules. Clinics are usually open between 8:30 a.m. and 5 p.m. and outpatient visits are widely scattered in between. Emergency outpatient services are available at all times.

Another category of persons who add to the traffic activity of hospitals is made up of those who visit the sick. Visiting hours vary among hospitals and among units of the same hospital. In general, visiting is allowed between 11 a.m. and 2 p.m. and between 4 p.m. and 8 p.m. Reliable relationships of the number of visitors and the number of patients, bed occupancy, or number of beds have not been established.

The combined outpatient and visitor components may account for as much as one-third, or more, of the traffic activities at hospitals. The large variation in the number and time of these trips among different hospitals may account for much of the discrepancy in the predictive formulas developed later.

[3] *From Hospitals, J.A.H.A.:* Reprinted, with permission, from *Hospitals, Journal of the American Hospital Association* (Vol. 45, No. 15, Part 2, August 1971, p. 448).

Previous Studies

Little information is available on access and parking at hospitals. "Access and Parking for Institutions," published by the Eno Foundation for Highway Control in 1960, examined limited available data and derived a few general guidelines for hospital traffic planning.[4] A more recent study, "Access and Parking Criteria for Hospitals," published by the University of British Columbia, Canada, analyzed the traffic characteristics of 11 hospitals in metropolitan Vancouver.[5]

Other reports on hospital traffic are based on data collected for areawide transportation studies. In these cases, hospitals were only one of the multitude of trip destinations considered in the overall study. "Urban Travel Patterns for Hospitals, Universities, Office Buildings, and Capitols,"[6] published by the Highway Research Board is an outstanding report of this type. On-the-scene research of hospital traffic problems in the United States has been limited. And although several hospitals have retained consultants to study their traffic problems, few of these reports have been published.

Nature, Purpose, and Scope of Study

This study relies principally on data obtained from traffic and parking studies conducted for individual hospitals by consulting firms.[7] Other more limited data used in this study were derived from trip generation counts by the California Division of High-

4 Wilbur S. Smith, *Access and Parking for Institutions* (Saugatuck, Connecticut: Eno Foundation for Highway Traffic Control, 1960) pp. 15-17, 27-30.
5 V. Setty Pendakur and Paul O. Roer, *Access and Parking Criteria for Hospitals* (Vancouver, British Columbia: University of British Columbia, March 1970) 42 pp.
6 Louis E. Keefer and David K. Witheford, "Urban Travel Patterns for Hospitals, Universities, Office Buildings, and Capitols," *National Cooperative Highway Research Project Report 62* (Washington, D.C.: Highway Research Board, 1969) pp. 13-55.
7 The traffic data for the hospitals described in Table VI were obtained from studies conducted over many years by a traffic consultant. Reports of these studies are for restricted use and, therefore, will not be referred to individually.

TABLE VI—CHARACTERISTICS OF STUDY HOSPITALS

Hospital Data at Time of Study

Hospital Classification by Service[a]	Inpatient Data			Newborn Data		Personnel[b]	Hospital Location[c]	Date of Study[c]
	Beds[b]	Census[b]	Occupancy Percent[b]	Bassinets[b]	Births[b]			
General	798	645	81	90	2585	1573	Phila., Pa.	1963
General	1132	973	80	42	1767	2841	Buffalo	1965
General	395	340	86	44	1789	809	Buffalo, N.Y.	1965
General	526	489	89	125	3621	1133	Buffalo, N.Y.	1965
General	382	295	77	43	1689	823	Pasadena, Cal.	1965
General	823	611	74	88	7167	1975	Dallas, Tex.	1966
General	660	526	79	52	1939	2098	San Francisco, Cal.	1966
General	400	332	82	52	1644	941	Los Angeles, Cal.	1967
General	479	399	83	50	2013	1462	Winston-Salem, N.C.	1968
General	350	275	78	34	965	744	Greenwich, Ct.	1968
General	402	319	79	50	1563	907	Waterbury, Ct.	1968

TABLE VI (Continued)

Hospital Data at Time of Study

Hospital Classification by Service[a]	Inpatient Data			Newborn Data		Personnel[b]	Hospital Location[c]	Date of Study[c]
	Beds[b]	Census[b]	Occupancy Percent[b]	Bassinets[b]	Births[b]			
Children's	313	224	71	72	3047	1030	Buffalo, N.Y.	1968
General	627	587	94	43	1957	1763	Miami Beach, Fla.	1969
General	356	303	85	62	3022	1441	Boston, Ma.	1969
General	347	329	95	—	—	1242	Boston, Ma.	1969
General	321	291	91	—	—	1686	Boston, Ma.	1969
Children's	343	298	87	—	—	2268	Boston, Ma.	1969
Geriatrics	93	83	89	—	—	273	Boston, Ma.	1969
Maternity	264	192	73	183	6930	925	Boston, Ma.	1969
General	327	272	84	28	1563	701	Trenton, N.J.	1970
General	346	341	98	58	2143	1094	Buffalo, N.Y.	1970

a All hospitals are nonprofit and short-stay.

b From Hospitals, J.A.H.A.: Reprinted, with permission, from Hospitals, Journal of the American Hospital Association (various issues).

c See Footnote 7, p. 9.

ways and by an ITE local section.[8] The hospitals and medical centers studied, along with some of their characteristics are listed in Table VI. They are mostly nonprofit, nongovernmental, short-stay, general hospitals with bed counts ranging from 321 to 1,132. They include, also, several specialized hospitals.

Many hospitals are located within developed areas. The street system adjacent to these hospitals naturally serves other traffic as well. Care was exercised in this report to analyze only hospital traffic. This was achieved by limiting the traffic count data in the various reports utilized for this analysis to that obtained at hospital access points and parking terminals. The results of internal questionnaires related to hospital transportation only were also utilized.

The purpose of this study is to analyze the combined traffic data for the institutions listed in Table VI in an effort to establish criteria for the planning of general hospital traffic facilities. Unfortunately, the same traffic data were not collected at all of the hospitals listed. This has limited the size of the sample available for analysis.

In scope, this study includes the analysis and discussion of hospital traffic with respect to automobile utilization, traffic volume patterns, trip generation and parking. In addition, it attempts to describe the patterns of transit, taxis, trucks, and other traffic. It concludes with a description of the role of transportation considerations in hospital site location and planning.

GLOSSARY

General Hospital: For the purpose of this report, a general hospital is a nonfederal short-term hospital whose facilities and services are available to the entire community.

---

[8] H. K. Chang and C. L. Smith, *Sixth Progress Report on Trip Ends Generation Research Counts* (San Francisco, California: State of California, Business and Transportation Agency, Department of Public Works, Division of Highways, December 1970); also, private correspondence with Howard I. Reynolds, ITE Metropolitan New York Section, June 1971.

Admissions: Number of patients accepted for inpatient service during a 12-month period; does not include newborn.

Census: Average number of inpatients per day computed on an annual basis; does not include newborn.

Occupancy: The percentage ratio of census to beds.

Short-term (stay) hospital: Where over 50 percent of all patients admitted stay less than 30 days.

Long-term (stay) hospital: Where over 50 percent of all patients admitted stay 30 days or more.

Employee (personnel): For United States hospitals, excludes trainees, private duty nurses, and volunteers. It includes full-time equivalents of part-time personnel.

Hospital population: The summation of census and employees as defined above.

Chapter II

AUTOMOBILE TRAVEL CHARACTERISTICS

Person trips to hospitals originate largely within the immediate vicinity of the hospital and almost entirely within the metropolitan area. A 1970 study of person trips to the medical institutions in Back Bay Boston (seven hospitals of different types) revealed that 43 percent of the trips originated within contiguous areas, 39 percent within the remainder of the Boston area, 12 percent in other parts of Massachusetts, and 6 percent had out-of-state origins.[1] The same analysis also showed that *automobile* trip origin patterns parallel those of *person* trips with the Greater Boston Area generating 74 percent of the driver trips. Other studies confirm the fact that, on the average, most hospital trips are not particularly long in terms of either travel time or distance.[2, 3]

AUTOMOBILE UTILIZATION

Automobile utilization, or the percentage of all hospital trips made by automobile, for various trip purpose groups at general hospitals is shown in Table VII. Employee subgroups varied widely in their use of the automobile. Taken as a whole, the percentage of all employee trips made by automobile drivers varied from 56.3 to 61.5 percent. The percentage of visitors driving automobiles varied within a wider range, from 42.9 to

[1] *Traffic and Parking in the Medical-Center Area, Back Bay Boston, Massachusetts* (New Haven, Connecticut: Wilbur Smith and Associates, December 1970) p. 25.
[2] Keefer and Witheford, pp. 39–41.
[3] Daniel L. Drosness and Jerome W. Lubin, "Planning can be Based on Patient Travel," *The Modern Hospital*, April 1966.

TABLE VII—AUTOMOBILE UTILIZATION AT GENERAL HOSPITALS

Tripmaker	Percent of all Tripmaking by					
	Automobile Drivers		Automobile Passengers[a]		Number of Study Hospitals	
	Mean	Range	Mean	Range		
Employees	60.1	56.3–61.5	10.3	4.7–14.4	5	
Medical staff and faculty	93.6	84.5–100.0	1.4	0.0–3.0	5	
Nurses	67.8	53.2–76.0	15.0	6.9–15.2	6	
Administrative—accounting	72.9	64.9–81.0	3.2	3.0–3.3	2	
Kitchen—housekeeping	41.5	31.9–51.0	7.4	2.8–12.0	2	
Technicians	77.6	73.0–84.0	4.7	1.7–8.1	3	
Visitors and outpatients	62.6	42.9–75.0	13.7	4.0–22.6	5	
All	61.0	60.0–63.0	11.7	4.6–14.3	5	

Tripmaker	Automobile Occupancy		Number of Study Hospitals
	Mean	Range	
Employees	1.15	1.05–1.24	7
Medical staff and faculty	1.02	1.00–1.05	6
Nurses	1.16	1.12–1.22	7
Administrative—accounting / Kitchen—housekeeping / Technicians	1.27	1.05–1.57	6
Visitors and outpatients	1.26	1.05–1.38	5
All	1.19	1.07–1.25	8

[a] Does not include taxi riders.

Based on: data for some of the hospitals described in Table VI.

75 percent. The mean percentage value for both groups (combined) was 61 percent.

Automobile *passengers* accounted for about 12 percent of all person trips to the hospitals covered in Table VII and varied from 4.6 to 14.3 percent between the individual hospitals.

Medical staff and faculty used cars almost exclusively and carried few, if any, passengers. Kitchen and housekeeping personnel utilized automobiles the least. This reflects the influence of income on modal choice.

AUTOMOBILE TRAVEL PATTERNS

Monthly and daily (weekday) traffic activity at hospitals as a percent of the average month or weekday traffic activity for a given hospital exhibited little variation. Hourly traffic volumes at the study hospitals fluctuated widely but had similar cyclic patterns.

Monthly Variations

The composite pattern of monthly activity at hospitals in the United States for 1970 is shown in Figure 2. Monthly patient admissions and outpatient visits fluctuated within ±5 percent and ±7 percent of their totals for the average month, respectively. Assuming that the traffic activity of hospital personnel follows the pattern of patient activity, this consistency in monthly totals could be utilized for traffic planning purposes. The months with traffic volumes nearest the average month are October, November, and January and the peak traffic months are February, June, and September.

Sufficient long-term traffic data were not available for the present study and the percentages shown in Figure 2 could not be confirmed. The two general hospitals in Connecticut for which data were available in this study (see Table VI) reported that patient census during the summer months is significantly lower than for other months in the year. This does not concur with Figure 2. Therefore, the composite pattern of patient ac-

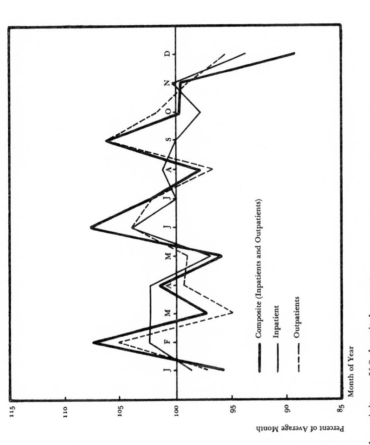

FIGURE 2. Monthly activity at U.S. hospitals, 1970[a]

[a] Pattern is corrected for differences in lengths of months and for the growth (between the beginning of the year and its end) of outpatient visits. The small growth in admissions was neglected.

From Hospitals, J.A.H.A.: Reprinted, with permission, from *Hospitals, Journal of the American Hospital Association* (various issues).

tivity (Figure 2) when used as an indicator of monthly traffic volumes must be applied with caution because individual hospitals may exhibit different monthly traffic variations.

Daily Variations

Daily traffic volumes at two general hospitals in Connecticut for which data were available for this study showed no significant differences between weekday traffic patterns. At one, weekday vehicular traffic totals varied within ±5 percent of the weekday average. The level of traffic activity on weekends and holidays was significantly lower.

Similar results were obtained from studies of daily traffic volumes at the medical institutions in Boston's Back Bay Area. For these hospitals, Table VIII shows that weekday vehicular traffic volumes were within 1.3 percent of those for the *average* weekday.

Hourly Variations

Hourly automobile traffic patterns differ among hospitals depending on their type and operational characteristics. Figure 3 compares the hourly traffic fluctuation at three hospitals of different types. The university and geriatrics hospital had pro-

TABLE VIII—DAILY VEHICULAR ACTIVITY: HOSPITALS
IN BACK BAY BOSTON, MASSACHUSETTS

Day of Week	Percent of Average Weekday Auto Drivers Only
Monday	101.3
Tuesday	100.2
Wednesday	100.6
Thursday	99.0
Friday	98.8
Average Weekday	100.0

From: *Traffic and Parking in the Medical-Center Area, Back Bay Boston, Massachusetts* (New Haven, Connecticut: Wilbur Smith and Associates, December 1970) p. 22.

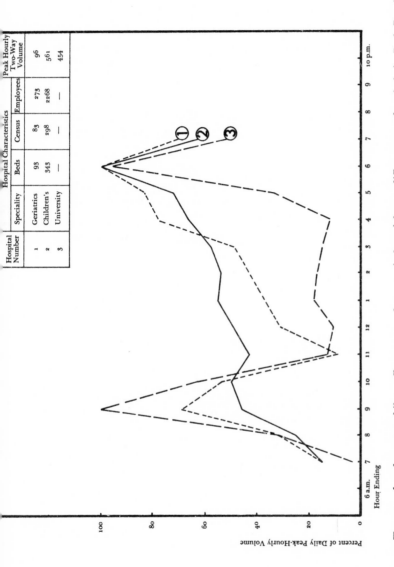

FIGURE 3. Two-way hourly automobile traffic patterns for a typical weekday at different type hospitals in Back Bay Boston, Massachusetts

Based on: data for two of the hospitals described in Table VI. The university hospital data were obtained specifically for this study from a consultant report.

nounced morning and afternoon traffic peaks while peak traffic at the children's hospital occurred only in the afternoon.

Figure 4 compares hourly traffic fluctuations at five general hospitals. Analysis of traffic activity by trip purpose for a Los Angeles general hospital (curve 1 on Figure 4) disclosed that an unusually large number of visitor arrivals and departures during the middle of the day accounted for the high level of midday activity. Taking this (and less pronounced scheduling differences among the hospitals) into account, Figure 4 displays some consistency in hourly traffic patterns for all of the general hospitals.

Figure 5 shows the inbound and outbound movement of automobile drivers by purpose of trip for one of the hospitals (curve 5, Figure 4). The morning peak traffic flow consisted mostly of inbound (day shift) hospital employees while the afternoon peak was made up of departing employees combined with the arrivals and departures of visitors and outpatients. The afternoon traffic activity was greater than the morning activity but was spread over a longer period of time. This is a weekday traffic characteristic of most general hospitals.

Peak-Hour Characteristics

Two-way peak-hour traffic volumes and average weekday volumes of hospital traffic are strongly related. Figure 6 shows this relationship at the 14 general hospitals for which peak-hour volumes were available. The linear regression line fits the data points with a coefficient of determination (r^2) of 0.90. The slope of the regression line is 11.7 percent—very close to the calculated arithmetic mean of 12.5 percent. This means that the peak-hour volume at general hospitals is about 12 to 13 percent of the weekday volume.

Directional Distribution

The hourly directional distribution of automobile drivers at two general hospitals is shown in Figure 7. The trend in

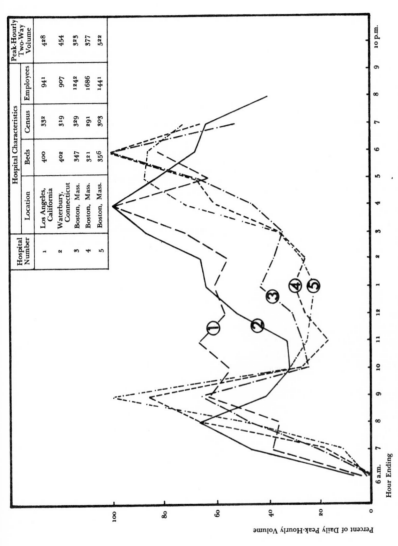

FIGURE 4. Two-way hourly automobile traffic patterns for a typical weekday at five general hospitals

Based on: data for five of the hospitals described in Table VI.

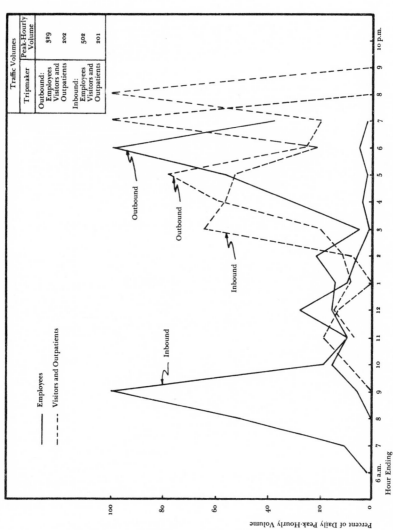

FIGURE 5. Hourly automobile traffic patterns of employees, and of visitors and outpatients, for a typical weekday at a general hospital in Boston, Massachusetts[a]

[a] The hospital had 356 beds and 1,441 employees. The census was 303 patients.

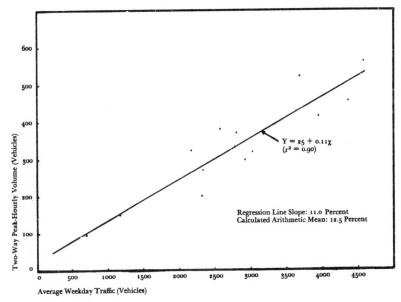

FIGURE 6. Relationship between automobile peak-hourly volume and average weekday traffic (AWDT)
Based on: data for some of the hospitals described in Table VI and for others (see Chapter I).

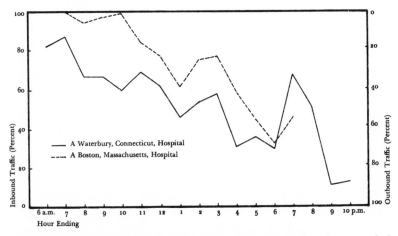

FIGURE 7. Hourly directional automobile traffic distribution for a typical weekday at two general hospitals
Based on: data for two of the hospitals described in Table VI.

directional traffic split for the two institutions is similar but the hourly ratio of outbound to inbound traffic is higher for one hospital than for the other. A predominant inbound traffic flow during the morning peak traffic period at both institutions is indicated.

Peak-hour directional split was analyzed for seven of the general hospitals described in Table VI whose two-way traffic peak hour occurred in the afternoon. Traffic volume in the direction of major flow (outbound) ranged from 56 to 83 percent of the two-way volume during the afternoon peak hour. In contrast, at an eighth general hospital whose two-way traffic peak hour occurred in the morning, inbound traffic was 96 percent of the two-way traffic.

Trip Generation

Trip generation rates based on single activity indicators are measured and used for traffic planning purposes because they are simple, easily applied, and are usually accurate enough for the problem at hand. Single indicators in use for hospitals include: the number of beds, the number of employees, site acreage, or floor area.

Site acreage and floor area have been demonstrated by others to be poor correlates to trip generation.[4] They are not used herein. The number of beds, the number of hospital employees, and total population (patient census plus hospital personnel) were the correlates to automobile trip generation developed in this report.

Automobile trip generation rates per hospital bed at 19 general hospitals (including those described in Table VI and others) ranged between 5.0 and 24.5 trips per weekday. For all 19 hospitals, they averaged 11.2 trips with 10.3 as the median value. Five of the 19 hospitals included in this traffic generation analysis had low levels of automobile utilization. These hospitals

---

[4] Keefer and Witheford, pp. 32–33.

were not included in the data used in the following analysis. The remaining hospitals had 58 to 62 percent of all person trips made by automobile drivers. Those hospitals whose percentage of tripmaking by automobile drivers fell within this range were assumed, for the purpose of this study, to have the *average* modal-split characteristics of general hospitals.

Automobile trip generation rates were computed for all of the general hospitals having *average* modal-split characteristics (and for which the necessary information was available). These rates and their ranges are shown in Table IX. The mean and median rates in Table IX have limited application because they are for a group of institutions and the amount of traffic activity at a given hospital will obviously depend on the size of the institution. This fact is demonstrated by Figure 8 which shows that (for the hospitals of Table IX) trip generation rates decrease with increasing hospital size (in terms of employees).

Linear regression analysis techniques were applied to the data summarized in Table IX to describe the correlation of automobile trip generation to the various indicators on the basis of hospital size. Figure 9 illustrates the correlation of average weekday vehicular traffic (AWDT) and the number of hospital

TABLE IX—AUTOMOBILE TRIP GENERATION RATES PER WEEKDAY AT SELECTED GENERAL HOSPITALS

| | Trips per Unit | | | Number of Hospitals |
Indicator (Unit)	Range	Mean	Median	Studied[a]
Beds	5.9–24.4	12.4	12.0	14
Population (Patient census plus personnel)	1.8–8.4	3.7	3.6	11
Employees (Personnel)[b]	2.4–11.7	5.0	4.8	11

[a] Only hospitals with average automobile utilization (58–62 percent of all person trips are made by automobile drivers) are included.

[b] See definition in glossary at end of Chapter I.

Based on: data for some of the hospitals described in Table VI.

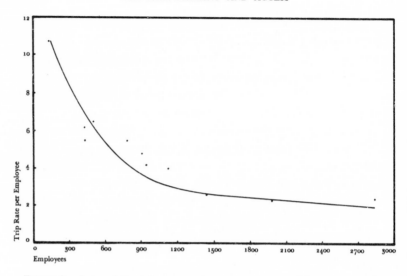

FIGURE 8. Automobile trip generation rates per weekday per employee versus number of employees at general hospitals

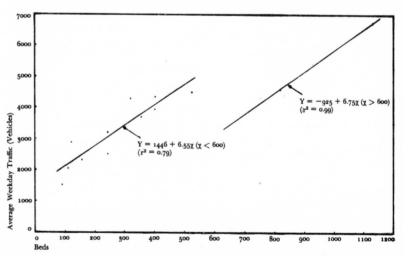

FIGURE 9. Automobile trip generation related to the number of general hospital beds

beds. Separate correlations were made for those general hospitals with less than 600 beds and those with more.

Figure 10 shows the correlation of average weekday vehicular traffic and hospital population. The hospital population used was the patient census plus the number of hospital employees. Separate correlations were computed for those general hospitals having less than 1,700 population and those with more.

The best correlation was obtained between average weekday traffic and the number of hospital employees (see Figure 11). Coefficients of determination, in this case, were 0.96 for those general hospitals having less than 1,200 employees and 0.99 for those having more.

PRIMARY TRIP GENERATORS

Automobile trip generation rates may be used for the overall planning of traffic operations and parking at hospitals. Large hospitals are frequently housed in a number of buildings covering extensive ground area. A study of primary trip generators within the hospital complex is required to plan the location and design of specific traffic facilities.

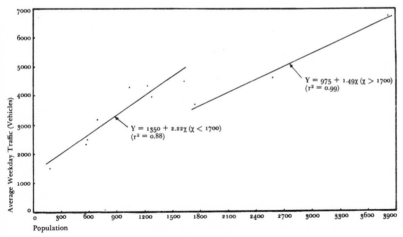

$$Y = 975 + 1.49\chi \ (\chi > 1700)$$
$$(r^2 = 0.99)$$

$$Y = 1350 + 2.22\chi \ (\chi < 1700)$$
$$(r^2 = 0.88)$$

FIGURE 10. Automobile trip generation related to general hospital population

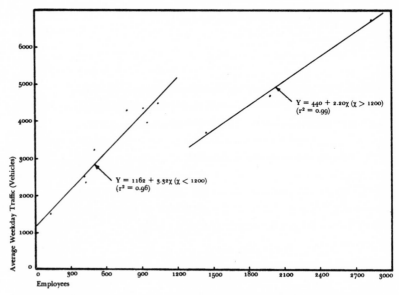

FIGURE 11. Automobile trip generation related to the number of general hospital employees

The information presented in this chapter demonstrates that the total number of automobile trips during an average weekday at a general hospital can be related to the total number of hospital employees. The distribution of these trips to various subunits of the hospital complex may be based on relative subunit activities when adjusted for the automobile usage characteristics of various hospital groups (see Table VII) and their time schedules.

This subroutine of traffic estimation and assignment may be a valuable aid in planning traffic access, circulation, control, and parking at and between the various units of the hospital complex.

Chapter III

PARKING

Parking is the most perceptible traffic problem around hospitals and one that elicits serious concern from their administrators. A parking shortage at a hospital may affect employee recruitment, may impede access to the hospital, and may strain the relationship between the hospital and the surrounding community.

Parking Supply

The supply of parking space provided varies greatly from hospital to hospital. There are two components of this parking supply:

1. Off street parking facilities—lots or garages that are hospital, commercially, or publicly owned; and
2. Curb spaces—located on public streets in the vicinity of the hospital and on internal hospital roadways.

The following analysis of both components is based on inventories conducted at 12 of the hospitals described in Table VI.

Curb spaces averaged about 30 percent of the total parking inventory around the 12 study hospitals. This percentage varied from zero (at three hospitals) to 78 percent (at a Philadelphia medical center). Most of the curb spaces were not metered and many were without parking time limits. Whatever restrictions existed dealt with peak-hour parking bans and with parking time limits.

Off-street parking spaces available in the immediate vicinity at the 12 study hospitals averaged 70 percent of the total parking supply. Most of these were owned by the hospital but some were provided by commercial enterprise and municipalities. At one hospital, for example, 310 parking spaces were provided in 11 lots. Most of the hospitals reserved separate parking areas for their medical staff but only a few designated separate facilities for the rest of their employees or for visitors and outpatients.

ACCUMULATION PATTERNS

Parking accumulation, the number of vehicles parked at any one time, is an important index of parking demand. Hospital parking accumulation patterns are characterized by a swift morning build-up, a flat all-day peak, and a rapid evening dissipation. This is usually followed by a minor peak in the early evening hours.

Figure 12 shows weekday parking accumulations in curb as well as off-street parking spaces at general hospitals. The composite pattern for 14 hospitals is shown as a solid line on this figure. Of these hospitals, the parking accumulation patterns of the two with the most divergent patterns are also shown on the figure as dotted lines. These indicate that the composite curve is essentially representative of each of the included individual hospitals.

The evening parking peak is about 65 percent of the maximum peak accumulation during the weekday (composite curve on Figure 12). This percentage varies depending on the size of the hospital—"The smaller the hospital, the higher the percentage" according to one source.[1]

Weekday parking accumulation patterns for hospitals of different types are similar to those for general hospitals. Figure 13 compares these patterns for a maternity, a geriatrics, and a children's hospital. Figure 14 compares them at three university hospitals. The similarities of all these patterns are attributed to the predominance of hospital employees in the parking population.

[1] Keefer and Witheford, p. 27.

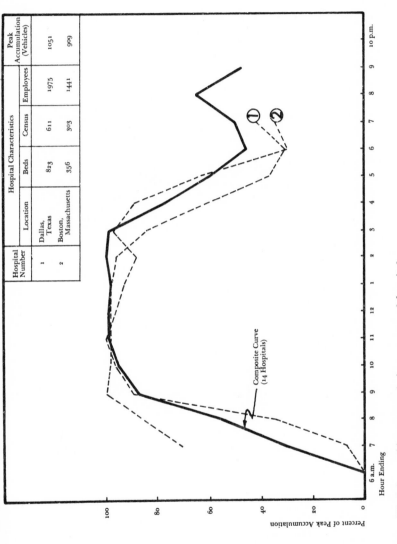

FIGURE 12.   Weekday parking accumulations at general hospitals
Based on: data for some of the general hospitals described in Table VI.

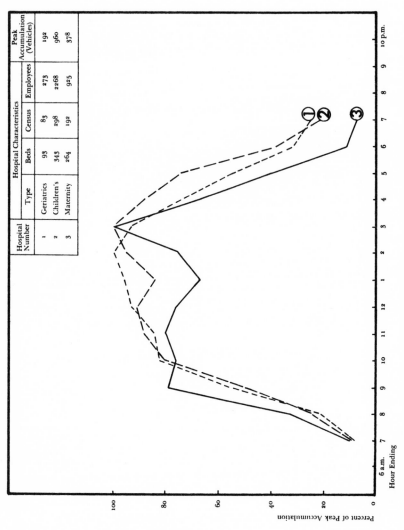

FIGURE 13. Weekday parking accumulations at different type hospitals in Back Bay Boston, Massachusetts
Based on: data for some of the hospitals described in Table VI.

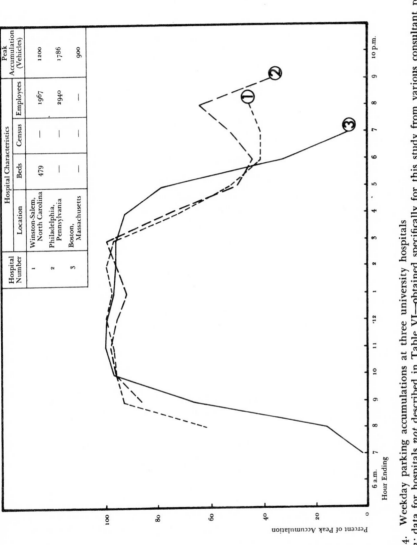

FIGURE 14. Weekday parking accumulations at three university hospitals

Based on: data for hospitals *not* described in Table VI—obtained specifically for this study from various consultant reports.

Weekday hospital *employee* parking accumulations are depicted in Figure 15. The composite pattern for nine general hospitals (shown as a solid line in Figure 15) resembles the composite pattern for *all* hospital parkers (Figure 12) except for the absence of an evening peak (after 6 p.m.). The two individual hospital patterns that were the most divergent of the composite group are also shown in Figure 15 and are similar to the composite pattern except for the slight peaking at the Los Angeles hospital during the shift overlap at 3 p.m.

Visitor and outpatient parking accumulation patterns vary widely at different hospitals. Figure 16 illustrates these variations. The Los Angeles hospital experiences afternoon and evening peaks of visitor and outpatient activity, while at the Greenwich, Connecticut hospital, visitor and outpatient parking accumulation builds up during the day to a major peak at 8 p.m.

For total traffic, *Saturday* parking accumulation patterns are similar to those for weekdays but *Sunday* experiences peak accumulations which coincide with visitor activities. Figure 17 illustrates these characteristics for a general hospital in Dallas. The amount of weekend parking accumulation is variable between hospitals. Saturday or Sunday peak accumulations varied between 44 percent and 102 percent of the weekday peak accumulation for a group of six hospitals.

DURATIONS

Parking duration at hospitals is primarily a function of trip purpose. Table X shows that, at six general hospitals, visitors and out-patients parked an average of 1.20 hours while employees parked an average of 7.30 hours. The corresponding averages were 1.97 hours and 7.00 hours for three and four university medical centers, respectively. Therefore, average parking durations for *all* types of hospital parkers combined at individual institutions would be expected to decrease with increase in the ratio of visitors and outpatients to hospital employees.

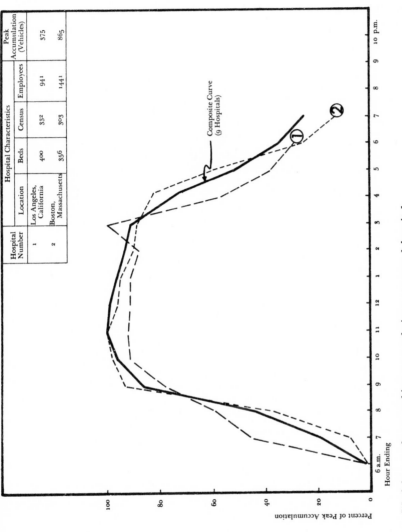

Hospital Number	Hospital Characteristics					Peak Accumulation (Vehicles)
	Location	Beds	Census	Employees	
1	Los Angeles, California	400	332	941	375
2	Boston, Massachusetts	356	303	1441	865

Composite Curve
(9 Hospitals)

Percent of Peak Accumulation

Hour Ending

FIGURE 15. Weekday employee parking accumulations at general hospitals
Based on: data for some of the general hospitals described in Table VI.

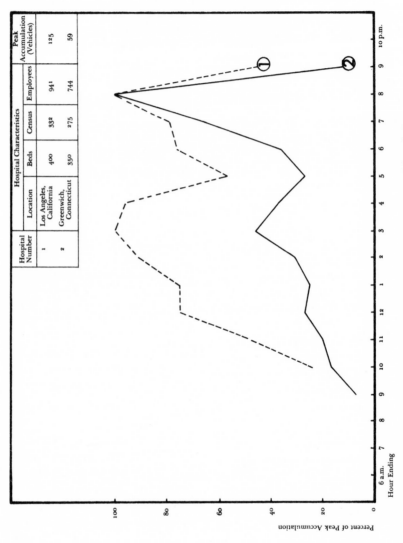

FIGURE 16. Weekday visitor and outpatient parking accumulations at two general hospitals
Based on: data for two of the general hospitals described in Table VI.

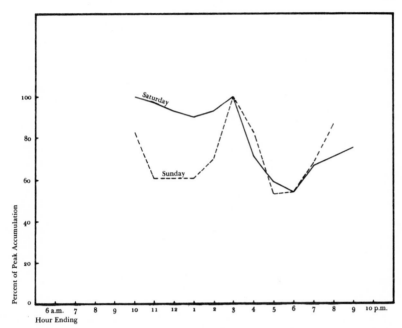

FIGURE 17. Weekend parking accumulations at a Dallas, Texas, general hospital
Based on: data for one of the hospitals described in Table VI.

Different hospital employee categories have dissimilar parking durations. An analysis of parking durations at a Buffalo, New York, general hospital described in Table VI revealed·that medical staff parked for an average of 3 hours, nurses for an average of 8.67 hours, and other hospital employees for 8.25 hours.

Table X also shows the average duration of hospital parking in curb spaces on public streets in the vicinity of two general and one university hospital. For both types, average curb space parking durations were less than half the average durations of parking in hospital off-street facilities.

WALKING DISTANCES

Table XI summarizes the walking distances of hospital parkers based on data from this study for a small number of

TABLE X—AVERAGE PARKING DURATIONS BY TRIP PURPOSE,
HOSPITAL TYPE, AND PARKING LOCATION

	Hospital Type	
	General	University
Trip purpose		
Visitors and outpatients	1 hr. 12 mins. (6)[a]	1 hr. 58 mins. (3)
Employees	7 hrs. 18 mins. (6)	7 hrs. 00 mins. (4)
Parking location		
Curb	1 hr. 40 mins. (2)	1 hr. 52 mins. (1)
Off-street	3 hrs. 32 mins. (2)	3 hrs. 33 mins. (1)

[a] Figures in parentheses refer to the number of hospitals for which the corresponding average duration was computed.

Based on: data for some of the general hospitals described in Table VI. The university hospital data were obtained specifically for this study from consultant reports.

hospitals. The distances are similar for both general and university hospitals. Employee parkers walked an average of 1.80 blocks. Visitor and outpatient parkers walked 1.20 blocks and shorter distances at night and on weekends.

TABLE XI—WALKING DISTANCES OF PARKERS AT GENERAL AND
UNIVERSITY HOSPITALS BY TRIP PURPOSE (IN BLOCKS)

	General	University
Employees (weekdays)	1.80 (4)[a]	1.80 (2)
Medical staff	1.60 (4)	
Nurses	1.75 (4)	
Other employees	1.90 (4)	
Visitors and outpatients		
Weekdays	1.20 (4)	1.20 (2)
Weekday nights	1.05 (3)	1.15 (1)
Saturdays	1.00 (3)	0.95 (1)
Sundays	1.05 (3)	1.05 (1)

[a] Figures in parentheses refer to the number of hospitals for which the corresponding average walking distances were computed.

Based on: data for some of the general hospitals described in Table VI. The university hospital data were obtained specifically for this study from consultant reports.

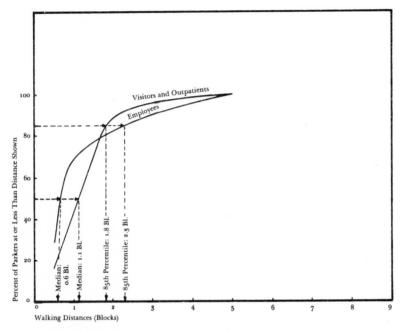

FIGURE 18. Cumulative percentage of weekday parkers by walking distances at a Buffalo, New York, general hospital
Based on: data for one of the several hospitals described in Table VI.

As would be expected, the walking distances of hospital parkers varies between hospitals. Figures 18 and 19 show the cumulative percentage of weekday hospital parkers by walking distances and purpose of parking at two institutions. At the general hospital, the median walking distance is shorter for hospital employees than for visitors and outpatients. The reverse is true for the university hospital.

Good traffic engineering practice reserves nearby parking facilities for short-term parkers while accommodating long-term parking in the farthest areas. Contrary to this, some hospitals allocate nearer spaces to employees—particularly nurses. One hospital administrator reasoned, "Parking is important when recruiting employees; we do not recruit visitors."

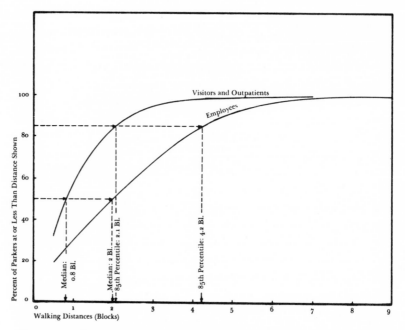

FIGURE 19. Cumulative percentage of weekday parkers by walking distances at a Philadelphia, Pennsylvania, university hospital

Based on: data for a hospital *not* described in Table VI—obtained specially for this study from a consultant report.

PARKING DEMAND

Parking demand for hospitals is assumed in this study to be equivalent to the peak parking accumulation of hospital traffic.[2] This peak accumulation of parked vehicles usually extends from 9 a.m. to 3 p.m. each weekday (see Figures 12, 13 and 14).

Parking demand (peak parking accumulation) varies directly with the size of the hospital and its activity, and with the degree of automobile utilization. It varies inversely with the ratio of visitors plus outpatients to average weekday hospital traffic.

[2] This obviously does not account for the "latent" demand of those who do not now come to the hospital but would, if parking were improved, or those who do not come to the hospital as automobile drivers because parking is not readily available.

To ascertain these relationships and to establish predictive equations, data from 18 hospitals were examined (Table XII). These included 13 general hospitals, a university medical center, two children's hospitals, a maternity hospital, and a geriatrics hospital. Except for the university hospital, for which data were obtained separately, these hospitals are described in Table VI. The grouping of these institutions of different types was considered to be desirable after investigation revealed no significant differences in the parking accumulation patterns among them, so as to increase the size of the sample used. The hospitals for which data were available varied in size from 93 beds to 1,132 beds and from 273 employees to 2,841 employees.

Simple parking indices, the ratio of parking demand to various activity parameters, were first computed (Table XIII). The mean indices per bed and per employee are very close to those recommended by a study of the Memphis Medical Center: "1.80 spaces per bed, or one space per 1.80 employees."[3] Using these single indices to predict parking demand, however, often yields results that are widely inaccurate.[4]

Regression analysis was also used in order to formulate predictive relationships between hospital and traffic variables, and parking demand. The resulting equations are shown in Table XIV along with the corresponding coefficients of determination (r^2). As additional variables were introduced r^2 increased. However, the regression coefficients fluctuated, though not widely, indicating the presence of not too severe multicolinearity problems. In this situation, it is, of course, theoretically desirable to use the equation with the highest r^2. From a practical point of view, however, the expense of measuring and using more vari-

---

[3] William H. Claire and Randall A. P. Johnson, "Planning for Memphis Medical Center Traffic and Parking," *Transportation Engineering Journal of ASCE* (New York: American Society of Civil Engineers, February 1971) p. 55.

[4] Table XV illustrates the divergence of observed values from those predicted using the mean bed, employee, and population indices. While the indices frequently give accurate results, the table reveals that there is danger in using simplistic rules for estimating parking demand.

TABLE XII—PARKING DEMAND ANALYSIS DATA

Hospital Number	Peak Parking Demand Y	Average Weekday Traffic X_1	Number of Beds X_2	Number of Employees X_3	Percent Occupancy X_4	Percent Auto Drivers X_5	Percent Visitors & Outpatients X_6	Population X_7
1	192	700	93	273	89	64	50	356
2	322	2338	395	809	86	60	52	1149
3	378	1656	264	925	73	49	61	1117
4	396	—	313	1030	71	65	35	1254
5	413	—	350	744	78	60	39	1019
6	476	4364	402	907	79	—	—	1226
7	499	3960	400	941	82	60	69	1273
8	507	2170	347	1242	95	49	44	1571
9	532	—	327	701	84	—	—	973
10	764	2584	321	1686	91	46	36	1977
11	850	3496	346	1094	98	73	41	1435
12	909	3698	356	1441	85	58	35	1744
13	960	4586	343	2268	87	50	36	2566
14	1050	4504	526	1133	89	62	54	1622
15	1071	4626	823	1975	74	63	45	2586
16	1200	—	479	2013	83	—	—	2412
17	1280	5690	627	1763	94	48	34	2350
18	1898	6736	1132	2841	80	60	34	3814
Average	761	3507	436	1321	85	58	44	1691

TABLE XIII—PARKING DEMAND INDICES AT HOSPITALS

Parking Index (Spaces per Unit)

Unit	Mean	Median	Range
Trip[a]	0.22	0.23	0.11–0.30
Bed	1.78	1.67	0.81–2.80
Employee[b]	0.57	0.55	0.38–0.93
Population[c]	0.44	0.41	0.28–0.64

[a] A single vehicle movement with origin or destination at the hospital (AWDT).

[b] In full-time equivalents; excludes trainees, private-duty nurses and volunteers.

[c] Equivalent to sum of employees (as defined above) plus average daily patient census.

TABLE XIV—REGRESSION ESTIMATION EQUATIONS FOR PARKING DEMAND

Equations	Coefficient of Determination (r^2)
1. $Y = -86 + 0.242X_1$	0.76
2. $Y = 72 + 1.580X_2$	0.72
3. $Y = 20 + 0.591X_3$	0.79
4. $Y = -76 + 0.495X_7$	0.86
5. $Y = -83 + 0.751X_2 + 0.391X_3$	0.86
6. $Y = -1101 + 0.909X_2 + 0.349X_3 + 11.915X_4$	0.95.
7. $Y = -1174 + 0.075X_1 + 0.685X_2 + 0.266X_3 + 11.810X_4$	0.96
8. $Y = -1113 + 0.104X_1 + 0.490X_2 + 0.263X_3 + 8.503X_4 + 4.019X_5$	0.965
9. $Y = 448 + 0.142X_1 + 0.497X_2 + 0.041X_3 - 0.405X_4 + 1.976X_5 - 11.063X_6$	0.974

Variables

Y = Parking demand
X_1 = Average weekday traffic (AWDT)
X_2 = Number of beds
X_3 = Number of employees
X_4 = Occupancy (inpatient census as a percent of the number of beds)
X_5 = Percent auto drivers of total person trips (automobile utilization)
X_6 = Percent visitors and outpatients of total person trips
X_7 = Hospital population (patient census plus employees)

ables must be weighed against the value of the additional information gained (or increase in r²).

Equation 6, where parking demand is related to the number of beds and employees, and to occupancy at a hospital, is therefore recommended as the practical method to use for the prediction of parking demand at general hospitals. Values for the variables used in this formula are readily available and the coefficient of determination is rather high (0.95).

Observed parking demand values predicted by Equations 6, 7, and 9 are shown in Table XV. Generally, predictions are more accurate for the larger hospitals with Equation 6 giving better

TABLE XV—OBSERVED VERSUS PREDICTED PARKING DEMAND USING
SELECTED REGRESSION EQUATIONS AND PARKING INDICES

Predicted Demand

Observed Demand	Equation 6	Equation 7	Equation 9	1.78 Spaces/ Bed	0.57 Spaces/ Employee	0.44 Spaces/ Person[a]
192	138	67	142	165	155	156
322	564	505	519	703	461	505
378	331	241	245	470	527	491
396	388	—	—	557	587	551
413	405	—	—	623	424	448
476	522	607	—	715	517	539
499	567	620	571	712	536	560
507	779	681	552	617	708	691
532	441	—	—	582	399	428
764	863	766	701	571	961	870
850	762	777	813	616	623	631
909	738	738	903	633	821	767
960	1038	1041	1030	610	1292	1130
1050	832	881	886	936	645	713
1071	1218	1142	1193	1465	1125	1137
1200	1025	—	—	852	1147	1061
1280	1204	1268	1322	1160	1005	1034
1898	1872	1816	1796	2015	1620	1678

[a] Of population as defined earlier.

predictions for the smaller hospitals than either Equation 7 or 9. The differences between predicted and observed values could not be attributed to any single factor. It is possible that one of these factors may be the inadequacy of the linear fit.

The influence of automobile utilization and of the percentage that visitors and outpatients are of total hospital traffic is demonstrated in Equation 9 where the first is shown to vary directly and the second inversely with parking demand. The impact, however, in terms of r^2 is slight. The institutions used for this analysis, however, had near average automobile utilization rates (see Table XII).

ZONING AND PARKING

Table XVI presents a summary of the zoning requirements for hospital parking stipulated for 166 cities. Requirements were set most commonly in terms of the number of beds. They ranged between 0.10 and 2.00 parking spaces per bed with mean and modal values of 0.69 and 1.00, respectively. A number of cities based their requirements on the hospital's gross floor area. Others used a combination of bases with beds and employees being most popular.[5]

The bed-based parking requirements for zoning shown in Table XVI are well below their counterpart parking indices shown in Table XIII. If single indicator zoning requirements must be used in the interests of easy enforcement, values nearer to those in Table XIII, namely 1.8 spaces per bed or 0.6 per employee are recommended. However, the present study has demonstrated the shortcomings of single indices as parking demand predicters. It is suggested, therefore, that they be used as a starting point, and that in individual cases all of the variables used in the regression analysis in this report be considered in establishing parking requirements. Such a require-

[5] David K. Witheford and George E. Kanaan, *Zoning, Parking, and Traffic* (Saugatuck, Connecticut: Eno Foundation for Transportation, 1972).

TABLE XVI—SUMMARY OF HOSPITAL OFF-STREET PARKING
REQUIREMENTS IN ZONING ORDINANCES, 1969

| Unit | Requirement (Space per Unit) | | | Number of Cities with Require- ments[a] |
	Mean	Mode	Range	
Bed	0.69	1.00	0.10–2.00	96
100 square feet of gross floor area	0.28	0.10	0.05–2.00	21
Bed plus employee[b]	0.36 + 0.47	0.37 + 0.42	—	22
Bed plus doctor plus employee	0.35 + 0.95 + 0.35	0.25 + 1.00 + 0.25	—	27
Total				166

a

Cities	Number	Percentage
With above requirements	166	80
With other requirements	21	10
With no requirements	20	10
Responding	207	100

b The mean requirement in this instance is read as 0.36 spaces per bed plus 0.47 spaces per employee. This requirement may not be compared with our population based indices.

Based on: data from a 1969 survey described in detail in David K. Witheford and George E. Kanaan, *Zoning, Parking, and Traffic* (Saugatuck, Connecticut: Eno Foundation for Transportation, 1972).

ment will be subject, in addition, to the community's policy on providing transportation facilities.

PARKING CHARGES

Current pricing policies for hospital employees are well below the level of economic self-sufficiency. Actually, a considerable portion of employee parking is free. There are, of course, other pricing objectives besides meeting the economic cost of parking facilities, and some of these may mean that economic concessions have to be made. Such policies, however, have discriminatory implications particularly since there are no indications that any institution subsidizes the cost of commuting by public transportation. The paradox here is that while the less affluent worker who cannot afford access is required to pay the full transit fare, the more affluent worker receives parking services that are paid for largely by others.

Chapter IV

TRANSIT, TAXIS, TRUCKS, AND OTHER TRAFFIC

Hospitals are served by several transportation modes besides the automobile. Many employees, for example, depend on mass transit where its level of service is high and the environment is favorable. Pedestrian trips constitute an important proportion of student and lower-income employee travel. Taxicabs are another important mode. Their trips are few, but they serve an important function. Emergency vehicle access to hospitals commands top priority. The ambulance routing should be as direct as possible, with the least possible number of traffic conflict and delay points. The movement of supplies and goods by truck is also essential to the proper functioning of a hospital.

TRANSIT

Transit service to hospitals carries with it the promise of alleviating many traffic problems, frequently through encouraging a reduction of parking demand. However, improvements to the typically available transit service are needed first, both on a system-wide basis and as specifically applicable to hospitals. The latter may include the provision of strategically located bus terminals within the hospital complex to minimize walking distances and increase the feeling of personal security. Hospitals may encourage transit ridership through subsidies of transit fares or through the provision of a hospital-owned transit service —such as a dial-a-bus system.

Time Patterns

Monthly, daily, and hourly arrival and departure patterns of transit riders at hospitals are similar to those of car drivers.

48

Hourly patterns exhibit slightly sharper peaking because so many employees use transit.

A composite of transit trips to and from general hospitals, shown in Figure 20, was developed from data for 59 hospitals obtained from 16 urban transportation studies. The peak hour of arrivals accounted for 17 percent of the daily arrivals while the peak hour of departures accounted for 21 percent of the daily departures. The highest two-way peak-hour volume, which coincides with the evening peak hour, is 13 percent of the total two-way average daily traffic. This is only slightly higher than the 12.5 percent average for vehicular traffic.

Utilization

Mass transit use for travel to hospitals is a function of trip purpose, tripmaker occupation and sex, car ownership, and

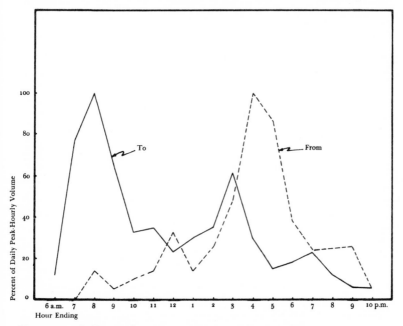

FIGURE 20. Daily transit trips to and from general hospitals
Based on: Louis E. Keefer and David K. Witheford, "Urban Travel Patterns for Hospitals, Universities, Office Buildings, and Capitols," *NCHRP Report 62* (Washington, D.C.: Highway Research Board, 1969) Figure B-9, p. 28.

TABLE XVII—MASS TRANSIT UTILIZATION BY TRIPMAKER CLASSIFICATION

	Transit Trips as Percent of all Tripmaking			
	Six General Hospitals		*Medical Institutions at Back Bay Boston, Mass.*[a]	*University Hospital, Philadelphia, Pa.*
Tripmakers	*Range*	*Mean*		
Employees	4.6–17.3	12.0	25.0	35.4
Medical staff and faculty	0–1.9	0.8	8.5	30.0
Nonmedical employees	8.5–31.6	21.6	33.7	57.2
Nurses	1.2–10.7	5.9		25.3
Visitors and outpatients	0.5–29.4	12.9	14.8	29.2
Students	—	—	19.0	19.0
All	2.3–20.8	12.7	21.4	32.6

[a] Including medical centers, and general and specialized hospitals.

Based on: data for six general hospitals described in Table VI; *Traffic and Parking in the Medical-Center Area, Back Bay Boston, Massachusetts* (New Haven, Connecticut: Wilbur Smith and Associates, December 1970) p. 23; and a consultant report on a Philadelphia university hospital obtained specifically for this study.

the character of the urban area as well as that of the immediate neighborhood. It is not sensitive to variations in hospital size and type.[1]

Table XVII illustrates the degree to which mass transit is being used by various tripmaker categories at six general hospitals, the medical institutions at Back Bay Boston, and a university medical center in Philadelphia, Pennsylvania. Nonmedical employees (the lowest income) use transit far more than any other employee group.

Medical staff, faculty members, and administrative personnel are infrequent users of mass transit. It is not surprising that

[1] Keefer and Witheford, pp. 19-21.

nurses use mass transit to a lesser degree than do most of the other employees. Others have found that female tripmakers are half as likely as male tripmakers to use mass transit.[2]

Visitors and outpatients vary in their use of mass transit. At a large general hospital in Miami Beach, Florida (described in Table VI) 38 percent of inpatient visitors came by transit, compared to only 14 percent of the business visitors and 12.5 percent of the outpatients. In another case a study, made available for the purposes of this report, of a San Francisco university medical center revealed that 47 percent of the outpatients came by transit, compared to only 19 percent of other visitors.

Consultants' studies at three general hospitals in Buffalo, New York (described in Table VI) and at a university hospital in Philadelphia, Pennsylvania, showed transit usage to be much higher for day visitors than for night visitors (6 p.m. being the dividing line). This may be due to the predominantly social nature of evening visits, while most day visitors are outpatients. In addition, less congested traffic conditions, availability of parking, less frequent transit schedules, and personal security considerations may result in higher nighttime car usage.

Other factors affecting transit usage include urban area size and travel characteristics, and hospital location. The larger the city and the better the transit service, the higher will be the proportion of trips by mass transit. On the other hand, higher automobile ownership within the region and lower density of population in the hospital neighborhood will lower transit usage. Also, hospitals located near a number of transit lines (as in the CBD) will be better served by this mode.

In one study of transit use at general hospitals it was found that "downtown hospitals are seen to attract about 29 percent transit tripmaking; intermediate hospitals, 14 percent; suburban hospitals, 9 percent; and outlying hospitals, 5 percent."[3] Another study, which divided hospitals into urban and suburban location categories, found that transit tripmaking was 19

2 Ibid., p. 20.
3 Ibid., p. 21.

percent for urban locations but only 10 percent in suburban locations.[4]

Transit usage also varies with trip origins. At the Boston medical institutions, 24 percent of trips originating in Boston and its vicinity, 5 percent of trips originating within other parts of Massachusetts, and 14 percent of trips from out of state were made by transit. The relatively high proportion of transit trips by out-of-state tripmakers was presumably caused by airline, bus, and railroad passengers utilizing the Massachusetts Bay Transit Authority (MBTA) for their local transportation.[5]

Other Trip Characteristics

The location of transit trip origins and trip length distributions are a function of hospital services and their availability within the community, the location of the hospital, and the size, character, and structure of the urban area. For centrally located hospitals in medium-to-large cities, the following trip characteristics may be hypothesized.

First, transit trip origins are concentrated in the "intermediate" area surrounding the hospital—that part of the high-density urban region which is beyond walking distance. This belt is likely to be the source of employees in the lesser-paying job categories and is also the region where transit service is usually most available.

Second, hospital transit trip lengths vary within the very short range of 1 to 4 miles. On the other hand, trip times will be twice as long, on average, as comparable automobile trips. Longer trip times are, of course, a major reason for declining transit ridership with increasing travel distances. Thus, transit trip origins per 1,000 population at various distances or travel times from the hospital exhibit a steep drop as travel distance increases.

From noncentral locations, trip characteristics could be different and the above hypotheses inapplicable. In suburban loca-

---

4 Pendakur and Roer, p. 23.
5 *Traffic and Parking in the Medical-Center Area*, p. 25.

tions, for example, hospitals may be so located as to be virtually inaccessible by transit. Service specialization at a hospital may also distort the above patterns since trips that would not have been made otherwise will result because of the special facilities.

Trip Generation

Transit trip generation rates, based on the number of employees, were computed for six of the study hospitals described in Table VI. For employee trips, one-way trip rates ranged between 0.143 and 0.256 per employee, and averaged 0.174 trips. Trip generation for visitors and outpatients exhibited wider variations, ranging from 0.017 to 0.554 trips per employee and averaging 0.184 trips. This wider variation may be due to the higher sensitivity of visitors and outpatients to the quality of transit service.

TAXIS

Hospitals are major generators of taxicab trips. One study, for example, reported that the hospital complex surrounding the Massachusetts General Hospital generated 7.6 percent of the total taxicab fares in the city of Boston. The study noted ". . . between hospital visitors and newly released patients, the only type of practical, comfortable, economical conveyance, other than private vehicles, is the taxicab. . . ."[6] In the Chicago metropolitan area, taxi trips to hospitals and mental institutions constituted 3.1 percent of total taxi trips, while other medical and health services attracted 4.9 percent.[7]

Time Patterns

Composite taxicab hourly arrival and departure patterns for the general hospitals located in the Minneapolis—St. Paul

6 Kevin G. Barbera, "Introduction to the City of Boston Taxicab Industry," *Traffic Quarterly* (Saugatuck, Connecticut: Eno Foundation for Transportation, April 1972) p. 282.

7 Edward A. Beimborn, "Characteristics of Taxicab Usage," *Highway Research Record No. 250* (Washington, D.C.: Highway Research Board, 1968) p. 91.

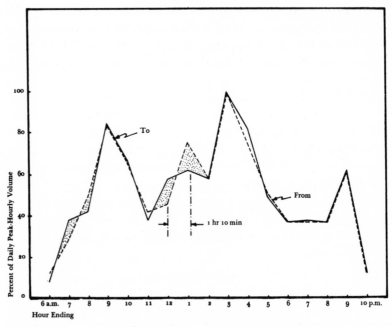

FIGURE 21.   Daily taxicab trips to and from general hospitals
Based on: Louis E. Keefer and David K. Witheford, "Urban Travel Patterns for Hospitals, Universities, Office Buildings, and Capitols," *NCHRP Report 62* (Washington, D.C.: Highway Research Board, 1969) Figure B-10, p. 29.

metropolitan area, Minnesota, are shown in Figure 21. Both exhibit mild peaking in the morning (8-9 a.m.) and the early afternoon (2-3 p.m.), with each corresponding to 12 percent of the total daily arrivals and departures, respectively. Patterns are similar in New York City and other places.[8]

Two characteristics of the above hourly patterns are of interest. First, peaking is less pronounced than that for automobile and transit trips, due to taxi usage by visitors and outpatients, whose trips are spread out through the day. Second, the overlap of inbound and outbound movement patterns clearly

8 "Who Rides Taxis?" *Regional Profile* (New York: Tri-State Transportation Commission, February 1969) p. 2.

points out that no long-term storage space is needed. An apparent exception is at midday when some short-term parking space is needed (see the shaded area in Figure 21) and the average waiting period is approximately 1 hour and 10 minutes. However, the expected peak number of taxis in waiting, under average conditions, is only two.

Utilization

Taxi usage at hospitals is influenced by taxi service availability and fares, transit service quality, household income and car ownership, and the level of congestion in an area. (Heavy traffic and shortage of parking space may make people reluctant to drive.)

The number of taxi trips made to 15 study hospitals described in Table VI ranged between 5 and 460 per day (for each hospital on a typical day) and averaged 108, with a median value of 70 trips. As a percentage of total person trips (by all modes and for all purposes) taxi trips ranged between 0.10 and 12.5 percent with an average of 3.08 and a median of 2.90 percent.

An earlier study reported an average number of 75 daily taxi trips, equal to 3.20 percent of daily person trips to general hospitals and 3.04 percent for university hospitals.[9]

It seems appropriate to assume, therefore, that a figure of three taxi trips per 100 person trips is a general planning guideline for short-term general, university, and other specialized hospitals (excluding mental and tuberculosis hospitals).

Taxicab usage varies widely by tripmaker classification (or purpose) as Table XVIII illustrates. It is highest for visitors and outpatients: 6.2 percent for the six general hospitals, 4.9 percent for the Back Bay Boston institutions, and 6.3 percent for a Philadelphia medical center. Employees differ as to the extent of taxi usage. Nonmedical employees use taxis the most and medical staff least. Students rarely, if ever, use taxis.

[9] Keefer and Witheford, p. 21.

TABLE XVIII—TAXI USAGE BY TRIPMAKER CLASSIFICATION

Taxi Trips as Percent of All Tripmaking

Tripmakers	Six General Hospitals Range	Mean	Medical Institutions at Back Bay, Boston, Mass.[a]	University Hospital, Philadelphia, Pa.
Employees	0–19.4	3.8	0.7	0.1
Medical staff and faculty	0–6.4	1.2	0.5	0.3
Nonmedical employees	0–25.2	5.7	} 0.8	—
Nurses	0–7.6	1.7		—
Visitors and outpatients	0.5–11.8	6.2	4.9	6.3
Students	—	—	—	0.1
All	0.5–12.5	4.7	2.1	2.0

[a] Including medical centers, and general and specialized hospitals.

Based on: data for six general hospitals described in Table VI; *Traffic and Parking in the Medical-Center Area, Back Bay Boston, Massachusetts* (New Haven, Connecticut: Wilbur Smith and Associates, December 1970) p. 23; and a consultant report on a Philadelphia university hospital obtained specifically for this study.

Other Trip Characteristics

Most hospital-destined taxi trips originate at home and a small percentage at transportation terminals. A study based on Chicago Area Transportation Study (CATS) data found that 50 percent of all urban taxi trips originated in residential areas and 7 percent in airports and railroad stations.[10] Considering medical trips only, the Lancaster Area Transportation Study revealed that taxi trip origins were exclusively limited to residential areas.[11] It is not inconceivable that many taxi trips to large medical centers (such as some of the institutions in Back

---

[10] Beimborn, p. 91.

[11] "1963 Traffic Patterns," *Lancaster Area Transportation Study*, Vol. I, September 1965, Table B.2.

Bay Boston) originate at airports, railroad stations, bus terminals, etc.

Trip production data revealed that all taxicab users (not only those that are hospital bound) make more trips per day than the average of the population of tripmakers. CATS data show, for example, that "the average taxicab user came from a household that made 7.46 trips per day, while the average household in the area produced 6.12 trips per day."[12]

Taxicab trips (to all land uses) were reported to be, on average, shorter than trips by other modes. In Chicago, their average length was 2.90 airline miles, while in New York it was 2.10 miles.[13] The average trip length is higher, 3.1 airline miles in Chicago, for social-recreational trips, a category which includes most hospital-related taxi trips.[14] In general, taxi trip lengths decrease as the intensity of surrounding development increases.

Projections

Currently, there seem to be few attempts to intensify taxi usage despite the ease of doing so and the benefits that can be realized.[15] There is small but strong demand for taxi service and this demand is expected to continue into the foreseeable future. No new systems, with the possible exception of demand-responsive systems, are thought to be able to substitute for taxi service.

Hospitals, therefore, should incorporate within their traffic plans permanent taxi passenger loading and unloading facilities. They should be so located as to assure maximum passenger safety and minimum obstruction to other traffic. If the hospital plans to rely on publicly provided stands, cooperation with municipal authorities is necessary.

---

[12] "Survey Findings," *Chicago Area Transportation Study*, Vol. I, December 1959, p. 115.

[13] Ibid., p. 120; and "Who Rides Taxis?" p. 3.

[14] Beimborn, p. 90.

[15] Martin Wohl, "Users of Urban Transportation Services and Their Income Circumstances," *Traffic Quarterly* (Saugatuck, Connecticut: Eno Foundation for Transportation, January 1970) pp. 42-43.

TRUCKS

Trucks are means through which goods and many services are supplied to hospitals. As such, despite their small number, they perform a vital transportation function. Their access to loading or unloading areas should be as free as possible of conflicts with other traffic. Their terminal areas should contain adequate loading and unloading facilities, waiting space, and dead storage space. When efficiently designed, truck terminal areas reduce the cost to the hospital of delay, pilferage, and breakage.

Time Patterns

Figure 22 shows inbound and outbound hourly composite trips to and from general hospitals in the Minneapolis—St. Paul

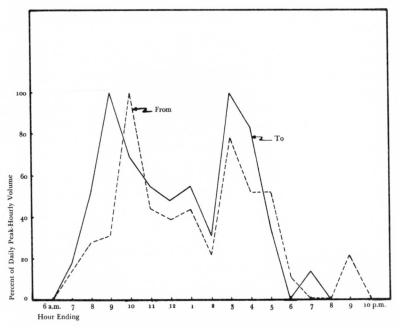

FIGURE 22.   Daily truck trips to and from general hospitals
Based on: Louis E. Keefer and David K. Witheford, "Urban Travel Patterns for Hospitals, Universities, Office Buildings, and Capitols," *NCHRP Report 62* (Washington, D.C.: Highway Research Board, 1969) Figure B-11, p. 29.

area. Peak arrivals occur in the morning between 8 and 9 a.m. and in the afternoon between 2 and 3 p.m., each corresponding to 15 percent of the daily traffic inflow. Peak departures occur in the morning between 9 and 10 a.m. and in the afternoon between 2 and 3 p.m. The morning peak departure volume, which corresponds to the daily peak, is equivalent to 18 percent of the daily traffic outflow. Inbound and outbound movements seem to follow closely, suggesting accumulations of small magnitude and short duration. The patterns shown in Figure 22 are similar to generalized truck movement patterns in several urban areas.[16]

Truck trip lengths, while varying by truck type, are generally short. 1958 Pittsburgh data showed that, by type, average trip length to land uses providing services (which include hospitals) was 1.37 airline miles for light trucks, 1.68 for medium trucks, and 1.00 for heavy trucks.[17]

Hospitals attract mostly light trucks. While general hospitals attract an average of 95 daily truck trips per hospital, only 25 of those trips are made by medium and heavy trucks (the latter figure is for all hospitals).[18] The high attraction of light trucks is further emphasized by another study which reported that the service and recreation industries (including hospitals) attract 10.2 percent of all light trucks making trips in an urban area as compared to only 4.4 percent of heavy trucks.[19]

Trip Generation

Previous studies have reported no correlation between truck tripmaking and the number of hospital beds or hospital personnel. However, total internal person trips (those originating within the metropolitan area) as well as total internal auto driver trips appear to be consistent indicators of the level of

16 Wilbur Smith and Associates, *Motor Trucks in the Metropolis* (Detroit, Michigan: Automobile Manufacturer's Association, August 1969) p. 49.

17 "Forecasts and Plans," *Pittsburgh Area Transportation Study,* Vol. II, February 1963, Table 31.

18 Keefer and Witheford, p. 21.

19 Wilbur Smith and Associates, p. 38.

truck activity, with one study reporting that general hospitals attract three to four truck trips per 100 person trips, or six to seven truck trips per 100 auto driver trips.[20] Truck trips at a Miami Beach general hospital (described in Table VI) averaged 2.6 per 100 person trips and 5.3 per 100 auto driver trips.

The difficulty in relating truck trips to measurable land-use characteristics complicates the task of planning for trucks and of establishing equitable off-street loading and unloading standards.

Loading Controls

Over the years, hospitals have become increasingly subject to off-street truck loading and unloading regulations. Nearly one-third of all cities exceeding 25,000 in population had such regulations in 1969, compared to only 11 percent in 1952.[21] However, little qualitative evolution of standards has occurred in the same period, and most standards still followed a 1942 recommendation of the New York Regional Plan Association.[22] According to the 1969 survey, loading requirements for most cities (63 cities) were based on the gross floor area of the hospital. Some were formulated in a graduated fashion (e.g., from 10,000 to 20,000 square feet of the hospital's gross floor area: one berth, 20,001 to 80,000; two berths, 80,001 to 150,000; three berths, etc.) Others offered formulas that were applicable once the hospital's gross floor area exceeded a certain minimum value, e.g., one berth for every 20,000 square feet, minimum: 10,000 square feet. Table XIX is a summary of both types of requirements combined. It gives the mean, mode, and range of values of gross floor areas that is required before an additional berth is called for.

Two methods can be used for establishing off-street loading and unloading requirements for hospitals. One is to use the

20 Keefer and Witheford, p. 21.

21 Edward Mogren and Wilbur Smith, *Zoning and Traffic* (Saugatuck, Connecticut: Eno Foundation for Highway Traffic Control, 1952) p. 46; and Witheford and Kanaan, p. 112.

22 Witheford and Kanaan, p. 116.

TABLE XIX—OFF-STREET LOADING AND UNLOADING REQUIREMENTS
FOR HOSPITALS, 1969[a]

Number of Berths	Gross Floor Area at Which Numbers of Berths is Required (in 1,000 square feet)		
	Mean	Mode	Range
1	12	10	0–80
2	82	20	10–300
3	139	40	20–600
4	223	60	30–900
5	311	80	40–1200
6	413	100	50–1500

[a]

Cities	Number	Percentage
With above requirements	63	29
With other requirements	7	3
With no requirements	146	68
Responding	216	100

Based on: data from a 1969 survey described in detail in David K. Witheford and George E. Kanaan, *Zoning, Parking, and Traffic* (Saugatuck, Connecticut: Eno Foundation for Transportation, 1972).

summary of past experience (as shown in Table XIX) and to modify it according to individual local experience. The resulting requirements could be defended as commonly accepted, easily enforceable, equitable, as well as reflective of local conditions.

The second approach is the "developer responsibility approach." Here the onus is on the developer to provide fairly accurate projections of his loading and unloading needs and to show how he intends to meet them. The steps involved in the estimation are shown in another publication.[23]

Planning Considerations

Truck access and terminal facilities should be planned to insure maximum safety and efficiency at least possible cost and with consideration for minimal environmental intrusion (fumes, noise, etc.). Routing trucks through tunnels and into under-

23 Ibid., pp. 123-124.

ground service facilities has been a popular, though expensive, method for alleviating goods delivery problems. It has been implemented in several regional shopping centers and downtown redevelopment projects.

Advanced distribution systems for intrahospital goods movement could be used to intercept deliveries at a peripheral service facility. Many such systems have been conceived. One, the Destination Control System, can serve other functions as well, e.g., transport of meals, mail, refuse, etc.

Joint usage of loading and unloading facilities by hospitals located in the same vicinity has already been suggested. A study of the medical institutions of Back Bay Boston recommended such an approach and suggested that it be implemented with due consideration of traffic engineering principles. The site chosen bordered on the area and the facility was envisioned to perform a break-bulk function with small delivery vehicles used for internal distribution. The study noted:

> Truck loading facilities, intended to serve an individual institution, are frequently a poorly utilized investment in terms of being occupied for this purpose throughout most of the day. When the situation is encountered, joint-use, or common truck loading facilities may prove to be an optimum solution, particularly for bulk deliveries via large trucks . . . analysis should . . . evaluate the joint use of goods movements by type of commodity —drugs, linens, central supply, blood banks, etc., and weigh the benefits of such joint use against possible inconveniences in terms of service times between the joint-use location and point of ultimate consumption.[24]

PEDESTRIANS

Every trip begins and ends with walking. Yet the pedestrian is often forgotten among the traffic planner's other concerns. Both his access problem and internal circulation problem have been generally neglected, although the latter has received more

[24] *Traffic and Parking in the Medical-Center Area*, pp. 82-83.

attention recently. In both instances, the main concern is to provide the pedestrian with a safe, direct, and pleasant trip.

Access

Many people walk to hospitals. Students make the highest proportion of walking trips, but a significant number of employees, particularly those of lower socioeconomic status, also arrive at the hospital as pedestrians (Table XX). Students and low-status employees live closest to the hospital. A consultant's study of the University of California's Medical Center at San Francisco estimated that 68 percent of all students live within a 1-mile walking distance from the Center and that 80 percent of these students walk to the hospital as compared to 6 percent of those living between 1 and 2 miles.

TABLE XX—PEDESTRIAN TRIPS BY TRIPMAKER CLASSIFICATION

Pedestrian Trips as a Percent of all Tripmaking

Tripmaker	Five General Hospitals		Medical Institutions at Back Bay, Boston, Mass.[a]	University Hospital, Philadelphia, Pa.
	Range	*Mean*		
Employees	5.9–15.3	11.6	16.7	12.6
Medical staff and faculty	1.5–17.5	9.2	15.3	4.5
Nonmedical employees	8.1–26.0	15.5	16.2	14.9
Nurses	5.6–14.2	9.1		20.8
Visitors and outpatients	0.8–4.9	2.8	6.2	13.8
Students	—	—	40.0	40.0
All	4.9–8.9	7.2	14.5	19.0

[a] Including medical centers, and general and specialized hospitals.

Based on: data for six general hospitals described in Table VI; *Traffic and Parking in the Medical-Center Area, Back Bay Boston, Massachusetts* (New Haven, Connecticut: Wilbur Smith and Associates, December 1970) p. 23; and a consultant report on a Philadelphia university hospital obtained specifically for this study.

Pedestrian access could be made easier and more trips encouraged if the trip is made safer and amenities such as trees, rest areas, lighting, etc., are introduced. Specific considerations include:[25]

1. sidewalks designed to handle anticipated pedestrian volumes adequately and to prevent spillover onto roadways;

2. high visibility crosswalk markings at signalized intersections, across intersectional approaches, and wherever there is substantial potential conflict betwen pedestrians and vehicles;

3. pedestrian barriers to prevent the encroachment of pedestrians on vehicular roadways and to prevent them from crossing such roadways at hazardous locations or where they might pose serious impedement to the flow of traffic;

4. pedstrian signal indicators installed wherever the Manual on Uniform Traffic Control Devices for Streets and Highways (MUTCD) warrants are met;[26]

5. lighting of proper intensity at critical locations, as at intersections and on wide streets with heavy traffic volumes;

6. safety zones and islands provided according to the MUTCD standards;[27]

7. pedestrian tunnels and overpasses where justified by high volumes of conflicting vehicular and pedestrian traffic; and

8. signs, markings, and police control to supplement other features.

Circulation

The internal circulation of pedestrians at hospitals complements all the primary travel modes discussed so far. Most tripmakers terminate their trips at some distance from their ultimate destinations; the last part of their trip is invariably made on foot. This can affect the choice of the primary mode. For

[25] For more details see Jason C. Yu, "Pedestrian Accident Prevention," *Traffic Quarterly,* July 1971, pp. 393-396.

[26] *Manual on Uniform Traffic Control Devices* (Washington, D.C.: U.S. Department of Transportation, 1971) pp. 241-245.

[27] Ibid., pp. 259-260.

example, if walking is made easier for bus riders than for automobile drivers, a shift in mode may be effected.

In addition to being made safe, direct, and pleasant, the pedestrian trip can be made faster through the introduction of moving belts or other technologies currently in development, parking lots and bus stops could then be located at greater distances, and perhaps be made more economically feasible as a result.

Improving the Walking Trip

The most important consideration here is to keep pedestrian trip distances within those limits which people are willing to accept—a willingness which decreases constantly from 900 to 1,200 feet and ceases at 3,000 feet.[28] For hospitals, it has been suggested that walking trips be kept under 600 feet for visitors and outpatients, and under 800 feet for employees.[29] These criteria should, in the absence of supplemental movement systems, govern the design of the hospital complex and the location of parking facilities. Parking rates are a related consideration. They should be negatively correlated with walking distances.[30]

Pedestrians should be encouraged to follow desired routes and discouraged elsewhere. In this respect the following comment by Lovemark is applicable:

> It is just as important to make the pedestrian system convenient and clear, as it is to make the mixed system or the pure vehicular system inconvenient for the pedestrian, even when this increases trip lengths for the pedestrian.[31]

Other factors include protection from inclement weather, snow removal, good drainage, and adequate illumination.

28 O. Lovemark, "New Approaches to Pedestrian Problems: Implications from Studies of Pedestrian Behavior," in *Transportation Systems for Major Activity Centers* (Paris, France: Organisation for Economic Cooperation and Development, April 1970) p. 52.

29 *Traffic and Parking in the Medical-Center Area*, pp. 80-81.

30 O. Lovemark, p. 53.

31 Ibid., p. 57.

The above considerations apply to all pedestrians including those originating from, and destined to, bus stops and parking facilities. It is not valid to assume that transit users are ready to walk longer or in a less desirable environment than automobile drivers. In both cases, pedestrians desire convenience, and both cases underestimate the dangers at conflict points with vehicles.

EMERGENCY VEHICLES

Usually few vehicles are destined to the emergency ward of a hospital. Increased traffic, however, will undoubtedly result from the expanding role that these wards are playing in satisfying the total health needs of the community. This new role has resulted in a shift in "the focus of ambulatory care, especially emergency care, from the physician's office to hospital clinics and emergency wards, where diagnosis and care can be undertaken more expeditiously and conveniently."[32]

Access

Emergency departments have traditionally been planned in relation to (1) outside hospital entrance, (2) x-ray department, (3) surgical suite, (4) medical records, (5) laboratory, and administrative offices.[33] The importance attached to access when planning emergency units is clear—a fact that is further emphasized by a recurrent rule in hospital planning literature which states that "ambulance and unofficial emergency vehicles must be able to reach the emergency entrance without complication once they are on hospital property."[34]

Applying this principle means that once emergency vehicles are within the main gate, the route to the ward should be di-

32 Delbert L. Price, "Ambulatory Care Facilities," in Alden B. Mills, Ed., *Functional Planning of General Hospitals* (New York: McGraw-Hill Book Company, 1969) p. 187.

33 Arthur H. Peckham, "Traffic and Transportation Systems," in Alden B. Mills, Ed., *Functional Planning of General Hospitals* (New York: McGraw-Hill Book Company, 1969) p. 307.

34 Delbert L. Price, p. 185.

rect with as few turns and points of conflict as possible. This access route should also be well signed.

Since the emergency unit entrance should be located so as to minimize the chances of blockage, it should be positioned downstream and as far as·possible from signalized intersections.

In general, good access and ample parking should alleviate the most important problems of emergency access. Insufficient parking, for example, would result in visitors and employees hunting for an on-street parking place, aggravating the traffic situation, and blocking the path for emergency vehicles.

Storage and Reservoir Space

Little is known about vehicle accumulations around emergency departments—whether of those parked while being serviced or of those waiting in line to unload a patient. Both, however, create problems that should be reckoned with.

Parking in the vicinity of the emergency unit should be available for doctors and for unofficial and emergency vehicles transporting patients. Most of these parkers are short term. This was evidenced by a study conducted at the Greenwich, Connecticut, general hospital (described in Table VI) which showed that the emergency room parking lot had the highest turnover rate (4.26) of all hospital parking facilities.

Reservoir space should be provided in accordance with the expected arrival rate, service time, and number of service bays. Adequate reservoir space is important, otherwise, lines of cars waiting to be serviced might get too long, blocking entrances and roadways and spilling over onto city streets.

Chapter V

TRAFFIC CONSIDERATIONS IN HOSPITAL PLANNING

The spread of areawide metropolitan health facility planning agencies has been one of the significant sociological and medical developments of recent years. It was abetted when Congress passed the Comprehensive Health Planning Act of 1966 providing for the coordination of all state health planning agencies and functions. Its growth was prompted by two factors; the increasing complexity and rising costs of medical care, and the failure of planning agencies to consider adequately accessibility to the medical and social service subsystems necessary to support an urban complex.

There are two traffic considerations of concern in the hospital planning process. First, there are the three planning inputs: accessibility considerations (such as travel time, cost, or distance), the need for sufficient land to meet hospital parking needs, and consideration of the impact of highways on the hospital environment. Second, there is the concern of correctly estimating hospital-generated traffic impacts on the surrounding transport facilities, particularly when hospitals are clustered in one location.

These aspects of hospital planning are examined in this chapter. The current distribution of health resources and the imbalance between supply and demand created by an outward moving population and a hospital system with fixed locations are reviewed. Other trends in hospital planning and in the evolving relationship between health facility planning agencies and city planning departments are also briefly noted.

TRAFFIC INPUTS IN HOSPITAL PLANNING

The importance of transportation inputs and their constraints on hospital location planning cannot be overemphasized. Hospital planners have devised methodologies for locating hospitals based entirely on transportation inputs (travel time, distance, and cost). However, constraints to such solutions include the need for an adequate supply of land to meet parking demands and the necessity of alleviating the impact of neighboring traffic arteries on the hospital environment.

Physical Accessibility Considerations

Accessibility determines in part the amount of travel at a given location (attractiveness is the other determinant). It measures the locational advantage of a site—the ease and worth of traveling to it—with respect to given types of travel related activities. It may be thought of as having three dimensions: (1) the capacity and type of transportation facilities leading to and from a given site, (2) the propensity to travel or the inversely related rate of attenuation (travel friction) along these facilities, and (3) the geographic distribution of competing hospital services and the attraction of each.[1]

Maximizing accessibility is the objective of hospital planning methods that attempt to achieve optimal geographic and functional distribution of health resources in relation to the population served. In this regard two methods have been used: the "facilities-centered" and the "population-centered" approaches. In the former "a group of . . . hospitals is surveyed to define the population served by them," while the latter "is based on the analysis of the current patterns of hospital use by a defined population."[2]

[1] B. Pushkarev and J. M. Zupan, "Pedestrian Travel Demand," *Highway Research Record No. 355* (Washington, D.C.: Highway Research Board, 1971) p. 37; and Yehuda Gur, "An Accessibility Sensitive Trip Generation Model" (Chicago, Illinois: Chicago Area Transportation Study, October 1971) p. A2.

[2] Vicente Navarro, "Planning for the Distribution of Personal Health Resources," *Public Health Reports*, July 1969, p. 577.

The facilities-centered approach attempts to measure the locational efficiency of a hospital—defined as the "cost of operating a hospital which may be attributed directly to its location."[3] These costs include primarily the travel out-of-pocket and time costs incurred by various hospital population groups. They also include terminal out-of-pocket and time costs (parking, walking, and waiting). A decline in the locational efficiency of a hospital corresponds to a rise in travel and terminal costs, therefore, and is directly related to a drop in accessibility.

The evaluation technique involves dividing the hospital users into seven groups: physicians, employees, trainees, inpatients, clinic outpatients, visitors, and suppliers. Individuals in each group are assumed to prefer the hospital as closely located to them as possible, and are thus viewed as exerting a "pulling force" on the hospital. This force is a function of trip time doubly weighted to reflect the community's relative valuation of travel time and the average frequency of trips made by the individual.

For all groups of hospital users a point of minimum aggregate travel (PMAT) could be determined, using a process illustrated by the simple example given in Figure 23. Assume $a, b, c,$ and d to be the origins of four hospital users whose trip times are equally weighted. Their PMAT will be at e—the most desirable hospital location from their collective point of view. Assume further that h is the present location of the hospital. The vector h e can be interpreted as a measure of locational efficiency and is labeled the locational imbalance vector (LIVOR).

In the population-centered approach, the first step is to define geographically a subject population, and to determine their hospital bed utilization characteristics. Points of maximum accessibility within the area are then determined using transportation study data.[4] These points, defined in terms of travel time

[3] Jerry B. Schneider, "Measuring the Locational Efficiency of the Urban Hospital," *Health Services RESEARCH,* Summer 1967, pp. 154-168.
[4] Jerome W. Lubin, Daniel L. Drosness, and Larry G. Wylie, "Highway Net-

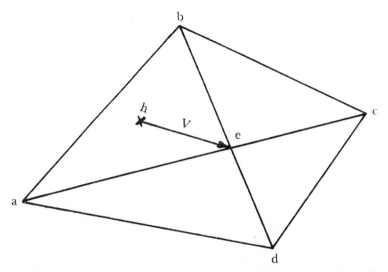

FIGURE 23. Determination of the point of minimum aggregate travel (PMAT) *e* of four hospital users and its relationship to hospital location *h*
From: Jerry B. Schneider, "Measuring the Locational Efficiency of the Urban Hospital," *Health Services RESEARCH,* Summer 1967, p. 157.

and travel costs, can be found by drawing equal time and equal cost contour maps. These are then superimposed on population density maps and the point having a minimum aggregate travel time is chosen as a location for the hospital.[5] Alternatively, hospitals may be located at the center of a service area defined on the basis of maximum traveling time irrespective of the population served.

Maximizing accessibility could lead to centralized locations close to central business district or to locations at junctions of major highways. Two previously mentioned traffic considerations, on the other hand, might lead away from such locations. These are land requirements for parking and environmental concerns.

work Minimum Path Selection Applied to Health Facility Planning," *Public Health Reports,* September 1965, pp. 771-778.

[5] Vicente Navarro, "Methodology on Regional Planning of Personal Health Services: A Case Study:Sweden," *Medical Care,* September-October 1970, pp. 386-394.

Parking Considerations

The availability of space for parking facilities must be considered by the hospital planner. Assuming a requirement of 1.80 parking spaces per bed (see Chapter III) and 300 square feet per parking stall, the land required for parking purposes exceeds 500 square feet per bed.

A tradeoff is possible between surface parking and underground and/or free standing garages. Construction expenses are weighed against land acquisition costs, aesthetic factors, walking distances, etc. This tradeoff will become a part of the larger question of balancing locational advantage and parking needs.

Environmental Considerations

Hospitals located near major highways are exposed to the potentially harmful effects of noise, air pollution, and vibrations. Visual intrusions as from massive structures and glare from headlights and luminaires are lesser problems.

Noise Pollution

A review of research suggests that general rules are not easily formulated. A large number of variables is involved. Some relate to hospital characteristics (its design and construction, whether central air conditioning is provided or not, etc.) and the design of its surroundings (trees, for example, are not effective noise attenuaters, but their psychological impact reduces the effect of noise. Others are highway characteristics (whether it is elevated, at-grade, or depressed, and whether noise reducing features are incorporated), traffic characteristics (speed, volume, and composition), and the horizontal and vertical separation between the highway and the hospital.

In general it does not seem that the impact of noise on hospitals is too great. A 1964 study of the noise environment at ten hospitals (nine located adjacent to major highways and the tenth close to the CBD of a major city) concluded that:[6]

6 "Noise in Hospitals Located Near Freeways," *Main Report*, U.S. Department

1. The average perceived noise levels due to traffic in typical patient's rooms varied from about PNdB (windows closed) to almost 80 PNdB (windows open). PNdB is the unit of perceived noise level, a measure of the "noisiness" of a sound.

2. The levels measured in the hospitals' corridors did not vary as much as the levels measured in the rooms, ranging from averages of 67 to 74 PNdB.

3. The patients were not particularly disturbed by traffic noise levels below 65 PNdB but were considerably disturbed by traffic noise levels above about 72 PNdB.

4. The interference by traffic noise with the duties of doctors and nurses was not considered severe in even the noisiest hospital and the interfering effects of other noise sources within the hospital appeared to be at least as great, if not greater.

5. The total hospital noise environment, regardless of traffic noise content, had little bearing on the recovery rate of patients and virtually no bearing on the doctor's decisions as to where he will hospitalize his patients.

6. The noise from freeways located adjacent to hospitals has not had a detrimental effect on occupancy rates, income, or expenses of hospital operation.

The foregoing conclusions give some indication of noise levels and their impacts. They do not, however, eliminate the need for special consideration of each individual case.

Air Pollution. Vehicular air pollution is undesirable around hospitals for obvious reasons. Fortunately, while pollutant concentrations are high at the edge of the roadway, they decrease exponentially (through atmospheric dilution) with increasing upward or outward separation. Figure 24 shows, that at distances of 160 feet from the edge of the roadway, concentrations are reduced by as much as 90 percent and that at an elevation of 100 feet reductions can amount to 70 percent.

of Commerce, Bureau of Public Roads, and Washington State Highway Commission, Department of Highways, January 1964, pp. 3-4.

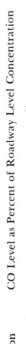

a. Pollution Level Versus Distance to Edge of Roadway

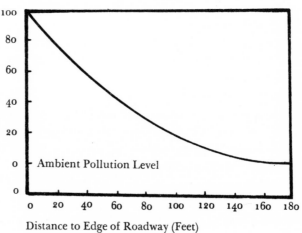

b. Pollution Level Versus Height Above Roadway

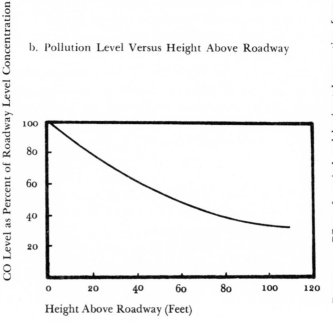

FIGURE 24. Effect of vertical and horizontal separation from roadway on air pollution concentrations From: S. J. Bellomo and E. Edgerley, Jr., "Ways to Reduce Air Pollution Through Planning, Design, and Operations," *Highway Research Record No. 356,* 1971, Figures 8 and 9. p. 150.

TRAFFIC IMPACT OF HOSPITALS

The hospital planner, the traffic planner, the zoning official, and the public all share an interest in ascertaining the extent of the traffic impact of a hospital on its neighborhood. Two aspects of the problem are important: first, the contribution of hospitals to the urban vehicle miles of travel and their demand for transportation facilities in their vicinity; and second, the unusual traffic patterns created in streets adjacent to clusters of hospitals.

Impact on Surrounding Facilities

The traffic impact of a hospital can be thought of on three levels of specificity: the metropolitan area, the local area, and the main access road. Three different measures can be employed at all three levels: vehicle miles of travel (VMT), the percent of 24-hour transportation facility capacity accounted for by hospital travel, and the percent of this capacity used during the peak hour.

A study investigating the impact of four selected general hospitals in Pittsburgh, Pennsylvania, found that hospital trips made up from 0.13 to 0.31 percent of total metropolitan area VMT. Hospital traffic accounted for between 17 and 48 percent of the main access road capacity on a daily basis. Peak-hour trips utilized between 28 and 64 percent of the main access road capacity. Thus, "hospitals may have slight traffic impact on the highway network at the metropolitan scale, yet may have significant, even critical, impact at the local scale."[7]

Impact of Hospital Clustering

The impact of a cluster of hospitals on traffic conditions on adjacent streets was investigated in a study of the Back Bay Boston area in Massachusetts. Hourly counts made on an internal street, Longwood Avenue, were compared with standardized hourly traffic variations derived from research

[7] Keefer and Witheford, p. 51.

conducted for the Institute of Traffic Engineers on 90 typical locations (Figure 25). The Longwood Avenue pattern, which exhibits little peaking, resembles that of a highly congested street. Instead, it is thought to reflect the patterns of institutional traffic. This becomes evident when the medical center's event schedule is superimposed on the pattern—the early morning peak is caused by a shift change of hourly employees at 7 a.m., when roughly 17 percent depart and 50 percent arrive. When that 50 percent departs at 3 p.m., it is reflected in related traffic volumes.

Clustering of medical facilities, therefore, can be beneficial from a traffic viewpoint. The daily traffic load is spread, more or less evenly, throughout the day making for a more efficient utilization of the street system.

DISTRIBUTION OF HEALTH RESOURCES

Interest in health facility planning has been spurred, in part, by the apparent chaos and irrationality that characterize the current distribution of health resources. More often than not, hospital service areas overlap and hospitals are in competition with each other. In addition, the failure of hospitals to respond to urban demographic change has resulted in the wrong services being offered at the wrong place for the wrong people, and in increased amounts of unnecessary travel for all hospital users.

Service Areas

The service area of the hospital reflects the extent of the hospital's drawing power and is defined by mapping the residential locations of its patients. Ideally, hospitals could be planned on demographic and accessibility criteria so that service areas will be geographically exclusive.

In actuality the service areas of established hospitals typically exhibit extensive overlap, as can be seen from desire line plots of hospital tripmaking. Explanations lie in the physician's role in determining where a patient is admitted, and the fact that

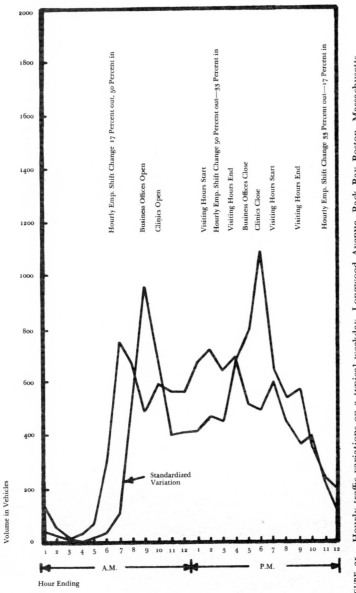

FIGURE 25. Hourly traffic variations on a typical weekday, Longwood Avenue, Back Bay Boston, Massachusetts *From: Traffic and Parking in the Medical-Center Area, Back Bay Boston, Massachusetts* (New Haven, Connecticut: Wilbur Smith and Associates, December 1970) Figure 4.

many hospitals are principally oriented to serve a specific, economic, religious, or ethnic group.

Locational Imbalance

Population shifts towards the suburbs, coupled with the inflexibility of urban hospital facilities, have created a serious locational imbalance that is constantly widening, as two studies of the Cincinnati and the Baltimore metropolitan areas show.

The first study concluded that "four large centrally located hospitals [in the Cincinnati area] . . . are (1) relatively poorly located and (2) apparently competing for substantially the same market area. The LIVOR's (locational imbalance vectors) of these four hospitals will probably become even longer during the next few years as population growth in the suburbs continues."[8] Longer LIVOR's mean longer travel distances and times and subsequently higher social costs.

The second study, made in the Baltimore area, drew similar conclusions. Table XXI summarizes the demographic characteristics and medical resources distribution by zone in that region. It is apparent that the centrifugal movement of the population to the suburbs was not accompanied by a similar movement of hospitals or even of physicians—who are relatively more responsive. Thus, more than half the beds in a large teaching hospital in Zone 2 were being occupied by residents of Zones 3 and 4 and not by residents of the neighboring community (see Table XXI).

Not only does locational imbalance affect patients, it also forces increased travel on doctors, nurses, other employees, and visitors. New hospital construction and institutional expansion through satellite hospitals should, therefore, aim at closing the widening gap between the service and the served.

TRENDS IN HOSPITAL PLANNING

The growth in the number of areawide hospital planning agencies and the widespread acceptance of comprehensive health planning augurs well for the future.

---

8 Jerry B. Schneider, p. 166.

TABLE XXI—DEMOGRAPHIC CHARACTERISTICS AND MEDICAL RESOURCES AVAILABILITY IN THE FOUR ZONES OF THE BALTIMORE, MARYLAND, STANDARD METROPOLITAN STATISTICAL AREA

		Demographic Characteristics		Medical Resources	
Zone Number	Zone Description	Percent of Population in Zone	Rate of Population Growth	Physician[a] per 1,000 Population	Acute Hospital Beds per 1,000 Population
1	Central business district	0.1	41.0	1.0	167.0
2	Inner areas of the city	22.0	−4.0	0.3	8.5
3	Outer areas of the city	24.0	4.1	1.5	4.1
4	Suburban	54.0	23.8	0.8	2.0

[a] Excluding specialists working full-time in hospitals.

From: "The City and the Region: A Critical Relationship in the Distribution of Health Resources," by Vincente Navarro, reprinted from *American Behavioral Scientist*, Vol. 14, No. 6 (July/August 1971) pp. 865–892 by permission of the Publisher, Sage Publications, Inc.

Even so, a primary step toward achieving better hospital services is through coordination of efforts between the hospital planning agencies and city planning departments. This issue was discussed in *Principles and Practice of Urban Planning*. While rejecting the idea that both functions could be borne by the same agency, the authors suggested three areas of cooperation:

The health agency can provide the planning agency with specific requests for the kinds of information it needs. The planning agency in turn can provide the information on population growth, characteristics, and movements; economic projections; land use; transportation and capital improvement plans; and other information that may affect the general planning of a health system and the development of particular sites. . . .

The planning agency . . . can review specific sites chosen by a health agency and make comments on their suitability relative to soil characteristics, availability of utilities, adjacent land uses, transportation and transit, and any urban renewal or development projects planned for the area. . . .

The planning agency and the health agency together can prepare a health facilities plan for inclusion in the comprehensive plan. . .[9]

Some of the information that the planning department can contribute to the health facility planning agency in the critical area of transportation has been suggested in this chapter. Traffic considerations will become more crucial as urban areas continue to grow.

[9] William I. Goodman and Eric C. Freund, Editors, *Principles and Practice of Urban Planning* (Washington, D.C.: International City Managers' Association, 1968) pp. 212-213.

Chapter VI

SUMMARY

During the past two decades, the accelerated usage of health facilities has created hospital traffic problems of growing intensity. The increasing activity of hospitals is evidenced by the increasing rate of patient admissions and of outpatients per unit of population, and in the rising employees to patients ratio. These, along with the increases in population and automobile usage, have had a multiplicative effect on the demand for access and terminal facilities at hospitals.

The traffic characteristics of hospitals vary among institutions of different types because they have different schedules, types of employees, and services. Among the various types, general hospitals are the most numerous. Traffic activity at these hospitals is directly related to the size of the hospital and to the activities of the various groups who serve and are served by the hospital, and who visit the hospital.

AUTOMOBILE UTILIZATION

The use of automobiles by different hospital tripmakers varies depending upon socioeconomic status as well as other factors. At the general hospitals studied, automobile usage by employees varied within the close range of 56.1 to 61.5 percent while visitor and outpatient automobile usage varied between 43 and 75 percent. For all person trips the percentage of automobile drivers varied within 60 and 63 percent and averaged 61 percent.

Automobile passengers constitute a small proportion of all person trips to hospitals. This percentage varies widely between general hospitals and the average for the study hospitals was

12 percent of all person trips. This percentage was higher for visitors than for employees.

Automobile Travel Patterns

Monthly traffic at general hospitals varies only slightly during the year. Peak traffic months of the year based on composite hospital activity indicators are February, June, and September for most general hospitals. Similarly, there is little difference between weekday traffic patterns at general hospitals but the level of activity is lower on weekends and holidays. Hourly traffic patterns vary somewhat between different general hospitals but their traffic peaking tendencies are similar. This is marked by a morning inbound peak hour made up of day shift employees and an afternoon peak hour consisting of employees plus visitors and outpatients.

Two-way peak-hour volumes and the average weekday volumes of traffic at the general hospitals studied were closely related. The peak-hour volume for two-way traffic at these hospitals was found to be about 12 percent of the average weekday traffic. However, the directional distribution of peak-hour traffic ranged from 56 to 83 percent in the direction of heavier flow at the hospitals where the peak hour occurred in the afternoon, and was 96 percent at the one hospital where it occurred in the morning.

Trip Generation

Trip generation rates at the general hospitals studied were computed on the basis of average weekday traffic volume related to: (1) number of hospital beds, (2) number of hospital employees, and (3) total hospital population. Only those hospitals having an average (58 to 62 percent) automobile utilization rate were included in this computation. The best correlation was obtained between average weekday traffic and the number of hospital employees. Coefficients of determination (r^2) in this case were 0.96 for hospitals with less than 1,200 employees and 0.99 for those having more.

Traffic problems often relate to subunits of a hospital complex. It is proposed that the total hospital trip generation may be properly distributed to subunits of the hospital when relative activities, automobile usage by different groups, and hospital time schedules are taken into account.

PARKING ACCUMULATION

This study investigated two components of the hospital parking supply: (1) off-street parking areas and garages, and (2) curb spaces located on adjacent public streets. Curb spaces averaged about 30 percent of the total hospital parking inventory for the hospitals studied.

Weekday parking accumulation at hospitals is characterized by a swift morning buildup, a flat all-day peak, and a rapid evening dissipation. The maximum parking accumulation occurred somewhere between 9 a.m. and 3 p.m. on weekdays and on Saturdays at the study hospitals. Sunday parking coincided with hospital visitor activities. The daily patterns of parking accumulation for employees at general hospitals were consistently repetitive and were similar to those of other types of hospitals. Visitor and outpatient parking accumulation patterns varied widely between hospitals.

Parking durations at hospitals are primarily a function of trip purpose. At general hospitals studied, visitors and outpatients parked for an average of 1.2 hours while hospital employees parked for an average of 7.3 hours. Therefore, average parking duration for all parkers at individual hospitals decreases with increases in the ratio of visitors and outpatients to employees.

PARKING DEMAND

Parking demand was assumed to be equivalent to peak parking accumulation for this analysis. Parking demand was found to vary directly with the size and activity of the hospital and its degree of automobile utilization, and inversely with the ratio of visitors and outpatients to average weekday hospital traffic.

Regression analysis was used to establish relationships between hospital and traffic variables and parking demand. For this analysis, data for 18 hospitals were used regardless of the type of hospital because their parking accumulation patterns were similar. Six hospital and traffic variables were used singly and in combination to compute nine regression equations for parking demand estimation. The closeness of fit to measured values was best for the equation using all six variables ($r^2 = 0.974$). However, the influence on parking demand of automobile utilization and the percent of hospital trips made by outpatients and visitors was less than expected. This may be due to the small range of reported values for these two variables. Whether this range is true for the majority of hospitals has yet to be determined. Meanwhile, usage of the equation with the three readily measurable variables—beds, employees, and occupancy—is considered to provide sufficient accuracy for parking demand estimation.

OTHER MODES

While the data available for the study were chiefly related to automobile traffic at various general hospitals, other modes of transportation were also discussed. These included transit, taxis, pedestrians, trucks, and emergency vehicles.

In general, use of transit by hospital tripmakers depends on the location of the hospital. For example, in one case, it was found that 29 percent of the hospital trips were made by public transit at downtown hospitals and only 5 percent at hospitals located in outlying areas. Transit usage also varies with trip origin. At the Boston medical institutions, 24 percent of the total hospital trips originating in Boston were made by transit while 19 percent of the total trips originating outside of the

Boston area were by transit. Nonmedical hospital employees (the lowest income group) were found to use transit much more than the higher income groups. The arrival and departure patterns of transit riders at general hospitals were found to be similar to those of automobile drivers.

Taxi usage varies widely among general hospitals. It averaged 4.70 percent of the total person trips at the general hospitals studied. Taxis are used more by outpatients and visitors than by other hospital tripmakers. Trucks are the only means for the delivery of goods and some services to hospitals. Total internal person trips as well as total internal automobile trips appear to be consistent indicators of truck activity. A Miami Beach hospital generated 2.6 truck trips per 100 person trips or 5.3 per 100 auto trips. Most truck trips were made by light trucks.

Pedestrians made from 4.9 to 19.0 percent of the total trips at the general hospitals studied. The number of trips to hospitals by walking varies with the availability of residential facilities within about 1 mile of the hospital.

HOSPITAL PLANNING

Much has yet to be learned about correctly considering traffic inputs into hospital planning. Most researchers have based hospital planning methodologies on travel time and cost considerations. What is lacking still is a comprehensive approach that will include *all* transportation related considerations such as terminal needs, environmental problems, etc.

In addition researchers have yet to correctly estimate the impact of hospital generated traffic and parking on the surrounding community. Some preliminary analysis has already been made. However, no conclusive results have been shown.

CONCLUSION

This study has been a preliminary attempt at filling the void of knowledge surrounding the traffic characteristics of hospitals.

It has relied on limited data to establish relationships covering automobile access and parking characteristics, and on assembly of material on the use of other modes. An attempt was also made to extend this knowledge into the hospital planning area.

A review of this study reveals many hypotheses that need factual support or repudiation. Obviously more data and further analysis are required. The field of transportation planning will be strengthened by such contributions to the understanding of this major traffic generator.